6 YEAR

Classworks
Numeracy

Series editors

Len and Anne Frobisher

Author team

Len Frobisher, Anne Frobisher

John Taylor, John Spooner, Thelma Page

Ray Steele, Mike Spooner, Anitra Vickery

Published in 2003 by:
Nelson Thornes Ltd
Delta Place
27 Bath Road
CHELTENHAM
GL53 7TH
United Kingdom

03 04 05 06 07 / 10 9 8 7 6 5 4 3 2 1

A catalogue record for this book is available from the British Library

ISBN 0 7487 7340 1

Illustrations by Tim Oliver
Page make-up by Hart McLeod
Cover photographs © Brand X Pictures/Getty Images and PhotoDisc/Getty Images

Printed in Great Britain by Ashford Colour Press

CLASSWORKS – BLUEPRINTS – LEARNING TARGETS – LASTMINUTELESSON.CO.UK

Nelson Thornes publishes teacher's resource books packed with flexible ideas for use in primary schools. As well as *Classworks*, Nelson Thornes publishes *Blueprints* and *Learning Targets*, providing busy teachers with unbeatable curriculum coverage, inspiration and value for money. We mail teachers and schools about new Nelson Thornes publications regularly. To join the mailing list simply photocopy and complete the form below and return using the FREEPOST address to receive regular updates on our new and existing titles. Books can be bought by credit card over the telephone or Internet. For more details log on to www.nelsonthornes.com or contact us on 01242 267 280.
For FREE resources register at www.lastminutelesson.co.uk

Please add my name to the Nelson Thornes Teacher's Resources mailing list.

Mr/Mrs/Miss/Ms _____

Address _____

_____

_____

Postcode _____

School address _____

_____

_____

Postcode _____

To: Direct Marketing Coordinator, Nelson Thornes Ltd, FREEPOST SWC 0507, Cheltenham GL53 7ZZ

Contents

Introduction

How *Classworks* works

What this book contains

- Visual resources for structuring mental, written and problem-solving work.
- Examples of modelled mathematical methods and solutions.
- Lesson ideas including key questions and plenary support.
- Photocopiable pages to aid and structure pupil work.
- Blocked units to slot into medium-term planning.
- Oral/mental starter ideas to complement the daily teaching of mental facts and skills.
- Every idea is brief, to the point, and on one page.

How this book is organised

- There are blocked units of work from one week to several, depending on the strand.
- Each blocked unit is organised into a series of chunks of teaching content.
- Each 'chunk' has accompanying suggestions for visual modelling of teaching.
- For many teaching ideas we supply photocopiable resources.
- The objectives covered in the units are based on DfES sample medium-term planning.
- The units are organised in strand-based chunks, in a suggested order for teaching.

Planning a unit of work

How to incorporate *Classworks* material into your medium-term plan

- Pick the most relevant unit for what you want to teach – the units are organised in strands, sequentially according to the DfES sample medium-term plans.
- To find the content, look at the objectives on the first page of every unit or just browse through by topic, picking out the ideas you want to adapt.
- Every page has its content clearly signalled so that you can pick and choose.
- Choose a generic starter from the bank at the back of the book, if required.

What each page does

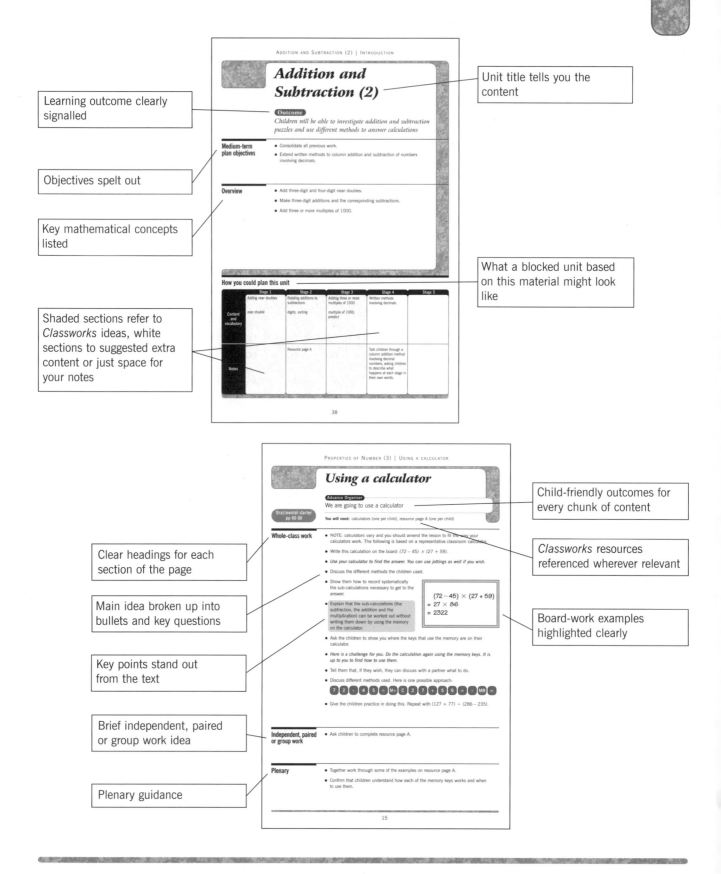

Learning outcome clearly signalled

Objectives spelt out

Key mathematical concepts listed

Shaded sections refer to *Classworks* ideas, white sections to suggested extra content or just space for your notes

Unit title tells you the content

What a blocked unit based on this material might look like

Clear headings for each section of the page

Main idea broken up into bullets and key questions

Key points stand out from the text

Brief independent, paired or group work idea

Plenary guidance

Child-friendly outcomes for every chunk of content

Classworks resources referenced wherever relevant

Board-work examples highlighted clearly

Properties of Number (1)

Outcome

Children will be able to multiply and divide decimals by 10 or 100, and use a calculator to check

Medium-term plan objectives	● Consolidate all previous work.
	● Multiply and divide decimals by 10 or 100, and integers by 1000, and explain the effect.
	● Develop calculator skills and use a calculator effectively.
Overview	● Multiply a number by 1000.
	● Multiply a decimal number by 10 or 100.
	● Divide a decimal number by 10 or 100.

How you could plan this unit

	Stage 1	Stage 2	Stage 3	Stage 4	Stage 5
Content and vocabulary	Multiplying integers by 1000 *multiply, place-value, digit*	Multiplying decimals by 10 or 100 *multiply, place-value, decimal number, digit, zero*	Dividing decimals by 10 or 100 *place-value, divide, decimal number, digit, zero*		
Notes		Resource page A	Resource page B		

1

Multiplying integers by 1000

Oral/mental starter
p 173

Advance Organiser

We are going to multiply a number by 1000

You will need: calculators (one per child or pair)

Whole-class work

- Draw on the board blank repeated multiplication by 10 diagrams, as shown.
- Ask the children for a single-digit number to write in the first four-digit blank number, say 6.

| | | | 6 | ×10 → | | | 6 | 0 | ×10 → | | 6 | 0 | 0 | ×10 → | 6 | 0 | 0 | 0 |

- *What is 6 multiplied by 10?*
- Invite a child to write the answer in the next four-digit blank number box.
- *What happened to the 6 digit when it was multiplied by 10?*
- *Where has the zero come from?*
- Ask the children to perform the same calculation using their calculator. Ask them to describe what happens.
- Repeat for the other two multiplications by 10.
- Discuss what happens to the digits of a number when it is multiplied by 10, by 100 and by 1000.
- Do the same for the start number 72.
- Extend the diagram to show multiplication by 100 and then 1000.
- Discuss the extended diagram with the children.

×100
| | | | 6 | ×10 → | | | 6 | 0 | ×10 → | | 6 | 0 | 0 | ×10 → | 6 | 0 | 0 | 0 |
×100
×1000

- Summarise the results using number sentences on the board.
- Do the same for 72. Let the children use a calculator to check each of the multiplications.

> $6 \times 10 \times 10 \times 10 = 6000$
> $6 \times 10 \times 100 = 6000$
> $6 \times 100 \times 10 = 6000$
> $6 \times 1000 = 6000$

Independent, paired or group work

- Ask the children to draw similar diagrams to explore multiplying 8, 2, 45 and 90 by 10, three times in succession.
- They can then find the answers to 67×1000, $3 \times 10 \times 10$, 5×1000, $84 \times 10 \times 100$, $1 \times 100 \times 10$, 328×1000, 4000×1000 and $659 \times 10 \times 100$. Encourage them to check each answer with a calculator.

Plenary

- Invite the children to explain how they answered the questions. Ask some of them to talk through their work at the front of the class.
- Ask others to take up the commentary at different points.

Multiplying decimals by 10 or 100

Advance Organiser

We are going to multiply decimal numbers by 10 and 100

Oral/mental starter
p 173

You will need: calculators (one per child or pair), resource page A (one per child)

Whole-class work

- Draw on the board a blank version of the repeated multiplication of decimals by 10 diagrams, as shown.

- Discuss with the children the place-value of each box in the three decimal numbers.
- Write in the 3 digit as tenths in the first number. Discuss why a zero is placed in the units box of this number.
- *What is 0.3 multiplied by 10?*
- Ask the children what to put in the second diagram. *What happened to the 3 tenths when it was multiplied by 10?*
- *Why do we not put a zero in front of the 3 in the second number?*
- Ask the children to check using their calculator. Complete the diagram for 3 × 10 = 30.
- Ask the children to check using their calculator.
- Discuss what happens to the digits of a number when it is multiplied by 10 and by 100.
- Repeat the activity for 0.41 and 2.97.

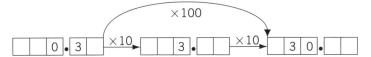

- You will need to discuss when it is important to use zeros and when they are not needed.

- Extend the diagram to include x100.

- Summarise on the board each multiplication as number sentences.
  0.3 × 10 = 3   0.3 × 10 × 10 = 30   0.3 × 100 = 30
- Ask the children to check using their calculator. Do the same for 0.41 and 2.97.

Independent, paired or group work

- Ask the children to complete resource page A.

Plenary

- Ask the children to show how they found the answers to the examples on resource page A.
- Stress what happens to the digits of a decimal number when it is multiplied by 10 and by 100.
- Draw the children's attention to how zeros are used and for what purpose.

(PUPIL PAGE)

Name: _____

Multiplying decimals by 10 and 100

Complete each diagram.

Check your answers using a calculator.

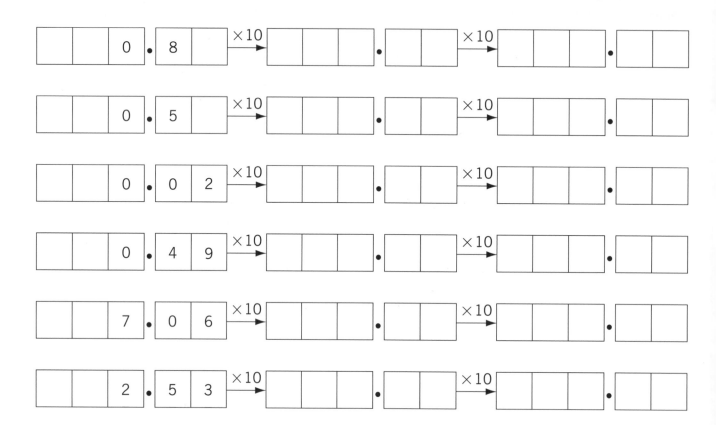

Find the answers.

$0.1 \times 10 =$

$1.9 \times 10 =$

$0.1 \times 10 \times 10 =$

$5.2 \times 100 =$

$0.1 \times 100 =$

$3.37 \times 10 =$

$0.08 \times 10 =$

$9.05 \times 100 =$

$0.04 \times 100 =$

$0.46 \times 100 =$

Check your answers using a calculator.

Classworks © Classworks Numeracy author team, Nelson Thornes Ltd, 2003

Dividing decimals by 10 or 100

Advance Organiser

We are going to divide decimal numbers by 10 and 100

You will need: calculators (one per child), resource page B (one per child)

Oral/mental starter
p 173

Whole-class work

- Draw on the board the blank repeated division of decimals by 10 diagram, as shown.

| 0 | . | 7 | | | $\xrightarrow{\div 10}$ | 0 | . | 0 | 7 | | $\xrightarrow{\div 10}$ | 0 | . | 0 | 0 | 7 |

- Discuss with the children the place-value of each box in the three blank decimal numbers.
- Write in the 7 digit as tenths in the first number.
- Discuss why a zero is placed in the units box of this number.
- *What is 0.7 divided by 10? What happened to the 7 tenths when it was divided by 10?*
- *Why do we put a zero in the tenths position in the second number?*
- Ask the children to check using their calculator.
- Complete the calculation 0.07 ÷ 10 = 0.007.
- Ask the children to check using their calculator.
- Discuss what happens to the digits of a number when it is divided by 10 and by 100.
- Repeat the activity for 2.1.

| 2 | . | 1 | | | $\xrightarrow{\div 10}$ | 0 | . | 2 | 1 | | $\xrightarrow{\div 10}$ | 0 | . | 0 | 2 | 1 |

- Discuss when it is important to use zeros and when they are not needed.
- Extend the diagram to include ÷ 100.

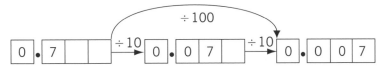

- Summarise on the board each division in number sentences.

    0.7 ÷ 10 = 0.07   0.7 ÷ 10 ÷ 10 = 0.007   0.7 ÷ 100 = 0.007

- Ask the children to check using their calculator. Do the same for 2.1.

Independent, paired or group work

- Ask the children to complete resource page B.

Plenary

- Ask the children to show how they found the answers to the examples on resource page B.
- Stress what happens to the digits of a decimal number when it is divided by 10 and by 100.
- Draw the children's attention to how zeros are used and for what purpose.

Name: _____

Dividing decimals by 10 or 100

Complete each diagram. Check your answers using a calculator.

| 0 | . | 1 | | | ÷10 → | | . | | | | ÷10 → | | . | | | |

| 0 | . | 5 | | | ÷10 → | | . | | | | ÷10 → | | . | | | |

| 3 | . | | | | ÷10 → | | . | | | | ÷10 → | | . | | | |

| 6 | . | 4 | | | ÷10 → | | . | | | | ÷10 → | | . | | | |

| 0 | . | 9 | 1 | | ÷10 → | | . | | | | ÷10 → | | . | | | |

| 8 | . | 0 | 2 | | ÷10 → | | . | | | | ÷10 → | | . | | | |

Find the answers.

0.6 ÷ 10 =   3.8 ÷ 10 ÷ 10 =

0.6 ÷ 10 ÷ 10 =   0.09 ÷ 10 =

0.6 ÷ 100 =   0.01 ÷ 100 =

9 ÷ 10 =   1.47 ÷ 10 =

2 ÷ 10 ÷ 10 =   2.54 ÷ 100 =

6.2 ÷ 10 =   8.03 ÷ 100 =

Check your answers using a calculator.

Classworks © Classworks Numeracy author team, Nelson Thornes Ltd, 2003

Properties of Number (2)

Outcome

Children will be able to investigate number patterns and generalise in words and in symbols

Medium-term plan objectives

- Recognise and extend number sequences such as square or triangular numbers.
- Count on in steps of 0.1, 0.2, 0.25, 0.5 and then back.
- Solve mathematical problems or puzzles.
- Recognise patterns and generalise.

Overview

- Use square numbers.
- Relate triangular and square numbers.
- Solve a mathematical problem involving consecutive numbers.

How you could plan this unit

	Stage 1	Stage 2	Stage 3	Stage 4	Stage 5
Content and vocabulary	Finding the sum and difference of two square numbers *square number*	Relating the sums of consecutive triangular and square numbers *triangular number, square number*	Solving a mathematical problem about the sum of consecutive numbers *consecutive numbers*		
Notes		Resource page A			

Finding the sum and difference of two square numbers

Oral/mental starter
p 173

Advance Organiser

We are going to use square numbers

You will need: squared paper

Whole-class work

- Draw on the board the first three square numbers, as shown on the right.

- *These shapes are the start of what sequence?*

- Remind the children of the square number sequence and how each number is written as a whole number squared.

- *Tell me the next number in the sequence.* Record *16* and *4²*.

- Repeat until 100 is reached.

- With the class, build the following grid for the addition of square numbers. Children should use squared paper.

- *What is 1 squared add 1 squared?*

- *What is 4 squared add 7 squared?*

- Record each answer in the grid in its correct position.

- Ask the children to complete the addition of square numbers grid.

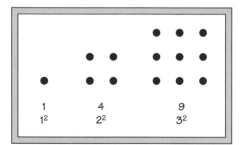

+	1^2	2^2	3^2	4^2	5^2	6^2	7^2	8^2	9^2	10^2
1^2	2									
2^2										
3^2										
4^2										
5^2										
6^2										
7^2			65							
8^2										
9^2										
10^2										

Independent, paired or group work

- Ask the children to construct and complete a similar grid for the difference between square numbers.

Plenary

- Build a table on the board, as shown. Ask the children for pairs of square numbers which make each number from 1 to 40 either as a sum or as a difference.

number	sum of two square numbers	difference between two square numbers
1		
2		
3		

- Discuss if they found numbers that can be made in more than one way as a sum or a difference of square numbers, and which numbers cannot be made at all in these ways.

Relating the sums of consecutive triangular and square numbers

Advance Organiser

We are going to use triangular numbers

Oral/mental starter p 173

You will need: resource page A (one per child and one enlarged)

Whole-class work

- Draw on the board the first three triangular numbers.

- *These shapes are the start of what sequence?*

- Remind the children of the triangular number sequence.

1	3	6
T(1)	T(2)	T(3)

- Explain the 'T' notation as the T meaning 'Triangular number' and the number in the brackets saying the position of the number in the sequence; for example, T(3) means the third triangular number, which has the value of 6.

- *Tell me the next number in the sequence.*

- Record *10* and *T(4)*. Repeat until 55 is reached.

- Use an enlarged copy of resource page A, the addition of triangular numbers grid.

- *What is T(1) add T(4)? How did you find the answer to the addition?*

- *What is T(7) add T(3)? How did you find the answer to the addition?*

- Record each answer in the grid in its correct position.

+	T(1)	T(2)	T(3)	T(4)	T(5)	T(6)	T(7)	T(8)	T(9)	T(10)
T(1)			11							
T(2)										
T(3)										
T(4)										
T(5)										
T(6)										
T(7)		34								
T(8)										
T(9)										
T(10)										

Independent, paired or group work

- Ask the children to complete resource page A.

Plenary

- Use an enlarged copy of the grid on resource page A. Ask the children for triangular numbers to complete the grid. Shade in the squares that hold square numbers. Discuss the patterns in the sums of consecutive triangular numbers and the shaded squares.

- Lead the children towards a general statement similar to the following: *The sum of consecutive triangular numbers is equal to the square of the larger of the two numbers.*

- Write this algebraic relationship on the board: *T(N) + T(N+1) = S(N+1).*

Name: _____

Square and triangular numbers

Complete the addition of triangular numbers grid.

+	T(1)	T(2)	T(3)	T(4)	T(5)	T(6)	T(7)	T(8)	T(9)	T(10)
T(1)										
T(2)										
T(3)										
T(4)										
T(5)										
T(6)										
T(7)										
T(8)										
T(9)										
T(10)										

S means square number. Write the square number sequence.

S(1)　　S(2)　　S(3)　　S(4)　　S(5)　　S(6)　　S(7)　　S(8)　　S(9)　　S(10)

Shade in square numbers in the addition of triangular numbers grid. Complete these statements.

$T(1) + T(2) = S(\quad)$ 　　　 $T(2) + T(3) = S(\quad)$ 　　　 $T(3) + T(4) = S(\quad)$

$T(4) + T(5) = S(\quad)$ 　　　 $T(5) + T(6) = S(\quad)$ 　　　 $T(6) + T(7) = S(\quad)$

$T(7) + T(8) = S(\quad)$ 　　　 $T(8) + T(9) = S(\quad)$ 　　　 $T(9) + T(10) = S(\quad)$

Write in words a general statement about the sum of triangular numbers and square numbers.

....

....

Compete this relationship: $T(N) + T(N + 1) = S(\quad\quad)$

Classworks © Classworks Numeracy author team, Nelson Thornes Ltd, 2003

Solving a mathematical problem about the sum of consecutive numbers

Advance Organiser

We are going to find the sum of consecutive numbers

**Oral/mental starter
p 173**

Whole-class work

- Write on the board the numbers from 1 to 20, in sequence.

- Ask the children to tell you two consecutive numbers in the sequence. You may need to explain what 'consecutive' means.

- *Tell me three consecutive numbers.*

- Repeat for four and five consecutive numbers.

- Invite a child to secretly think of two consecutive numbers and to tell the class only their sum. The child that says which two consecutive numbers give this sum, then chooses another sum.

- Record each sum on the board. An example is shown.

- Repeat this activity for three consecutive and then four consecutive numbers, as shown.

> $5 + 6 = 11$
> $13 + 14 = 27$
>
> $6 + 7 + 8 = 21$
> $11 + 12 + 13 + 14 = 50$

Independent, paired or group work

- Write the following headings in a table on the board and ask the children to copy and complete the table for each whole number from 1 to 40: *'two consecutive numbers that give that number as their sum'*, *'three consecutive numbers that give that number as their sum'*, and *'four consecutive numbers that give that number as their sum'*.

- If they cannot find sets of consecutive numbers that make a particular number, they should leave it blank (for example, 1 and 2 will be blank, 3 can only be made as the sum of two consecutive numbers, and so on).

Plenary

- Together, complete the additions of two consecutive numbers on a similar table on the board. Discuss what is special about numbers that are the sum of two consecutive numbers.

- Arrive at the generalisation: *The sum of two consecutive numbers is equal to double the smaller number, plus one.*

- Write on the board: $N + (N + 1) = 2N + 1$.

- Do the same for three consecutive numbers and the generalisation $N + (N + 1) + (N + 2) = 3(N + 1)$, which proves that any multiple of 3 can be written as the sum of three consecutive numbers.

Properties of Number (3)

Outcome

Children will be able to order and compare negative and positive integers, and use the memory on a calculator

Medium-term plan objectives

- Find the difference between a positive and a negative integer, or two negative integers, in the context such as temperature or a number line.

- Order a set of negative integers.

- Develop calculator skills and use a calculator effectively.

Overview

- Find the difference between any two numbers.

- Put negative numbers in order.

- Use a calculator.

How you could plan this unit

	Stage 1	Stage 2	Stage 3	Stage 4	Stage 5
Content and vocabulary	Finding the difference between numbers *difference, negative numbers, positive numbers*	Ordering negative numbers *negative numbers, least, largest*	Using a calculator *calculator*		
Notes			Resource page A		

Finding the difference between numbers

Oral/mental starter
p 173

Advance Organiser

We are going to find the difference between a negative and a positive number

---

Whole-class work

- Draw an unlabelled number line on the board.
- Invite the children to say at which position you should write 0. Point out that the number line goes in both directions: it shows negative as well as positive numbers.

0

- Tell them that the number line is a count-on-in-ones line.
- Select a positive and a negative number, say 3 and -4.
- *Where should 3 be written?* Extend the line if necessary.
- Discuss why, by counting on in ones from 0.
- *Where should -4 be written?* Extend the line if necessary.
- Discuss why, by counting back from 0 in ones.
- *What is the difference between 3 and -4? How did you decide?*
- Count up from -4 to 3 and then back from 3 to -4 on the number line.

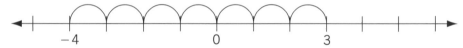

-4 0   3

- Write on the board: *The difference between -4 and 3 is 7.*
- Repeat the activity for other positions of 0.
- Rub out the 0 and reposition it near the right end of the number line and find the difference between -3 and -9.

-9 -3 0

Independent, paired or group work

- Ask the children to find the difference between various pairs of numbers, such as 6 and 3, 4 and -1, -2 and -5, 2 and 5, -3 and 3, -4 and -1. They can use a number line to support them.
- Then ask them to choose pairs of numbers (either negative or positive) that have a difference of 6. They should record six pairs of numbers. Ask them to investigate finding as many pairs of numbers as they can that are both less than 10 and which have a difference of exactly 10.

Plenary

- Invite the children to explain how they worked out the solutions to the questions.
- Discuss the investigation – how did they decide to work? Pick some examples of systematic methods and ask the children to explain what they did to the class.

Ordering negative numbers

Advance Organiser

We are going to put negative numbers in order

Whole-class work

- Draw on the board an unmarked number line.

- Write on the board: −12, −2, −7, −20, −9.
- Explain that they are going to find the approximate positions of these five numbers on the number line.
- *Which number do you think we should put on the line first?*
- Explain that a very good number to position first is 0.
- *Why is 0 a very good number to put on first?*
- Explain that 0 is the 'boundary' between positive and negative numbers.
- *Where shall we put 0?*
- Explain that as the five numbers are negative it is sensible to put 0 to the very right on the number line.
- *Which number should we put on next?*
- Explain that any of the five numbers can be put on next, but that −20 is a good one.
- *Why is −20 a good number to put on the number line next?*
- Explain that it is the smallest number and will be furthest of the five numbers to the left on the number line.

$$-20 \qquad\qquad\qquad\qquad\qquad\qquad 0$$

- In turn, invite some children to put on the line where the other four numbers will approximately be positioned.

$$-20 \qquad -12 \quad -9 \; -7 \qquad\qquad -2 \; 0$$

- *What is the order of the five negative numbers, smallest first?*
- Write them in order, smallest first.
- Repeat the activity with another set of negative numbers; for example, −25, −18, −10, −5, −3.

Independent, paired or group work

- Ask the children to draw number lines for the following sets of numbers, and to position each set on a separate line: −6, −17, −3, −14, −10; −40, −70, −10, −90, −30; $-\frac{5}{7}$, $-\frac{1}{2}$, $-\frac{2}{3}$, $-\frac{3}{5}$, $-\frac{7}{10}$.
- They should then, without a number line, write the following sets of numbers in order, largest first: −25, −15, −35, −5, −50; −9, −19, −31, −27, −8.

Plenary

- Together, work through the sets of numbers with the children, asking them up to the front of the class to draw a number line on the board with an appropriately positioned zero. Then ask the class to suggest where each number should go.
- Discuss how the children decided each time.

Using a calculator

Advance Organiser

We are going to use a calculator

Oral/mental starter
p 173

You will need: calculators (one per child), resource page A (one per child)

Whole-class work

- NOTE: calculators vary and you should amend the lesson to fit the way your calculators work. The following is based on a representative classroom calculator.

- Write this calculation on the board: *(72 – 45) × (27 + 59)*.

- *Use your calculator to find the answer. You can use jottings as well, if you wish.*

- Discuss the different methods the children used.

- Show them how to record systematically the sub-calculations necessary to get to the answer.

- Explain that the sub-calculations (the subtraction, the addition and the multiplication) can be worked out without writing them down by using the memory on the calculator.

$$(72 - 45) \times (27 + 59)$$
$$= 27 \times 86$$
$$= 2322$$

- Ask the children to show you where the keys that use the memory are on their calculator.

- *Here is a challenge for you. Do the calculation again using the memory keys. It is up to you to find out how to use them.*

- Tell them that, if they wish, they can discuss with a partner what to do.

- Discuss different methods used. Here is one possible approach:

- Give the children practice in doing this. Repeat with (127 + 77) ÷ (286 – 235).

Independent, paired or group work

- Ask the children to complete resource page A.

Plenary

- Together, work through some of the examples on resource page A.

- Confirm that the children understand how each of the memory keys works and when to use them.

Name: _____

Using a calculator

These are the calculator keys used for calculations. What are the calculations and their answers?

5 3 M+ C 8 1 + 1 2 6 × MR =

4 2 5 ÷ 8 5 = M+ C 1 3 0 + 6 5 = ÷ MR =

Use your calculator to find the answers. Write the keys you pressed to find the answers.

83 + (94 × 67)

516 − (899 ÷ 36)

(47 + 81) × (38 + 94)

(1380 ÷ 15) × (141 + 63)

(315 + 168) ÷ (966 ÷ 42)

Properties of Number (4)

Outcome

Children will be able to investigate prime numbers, multiples, prime factors and the products of odd and even numbers, and make general statements about each

Medium-term plan objectives	• Consolidate all previous work.
	• Recognise multiples up to 10×10.
	• Find simple common multiples.
	• Know tests of divisibility.
	• Recognise primes to at least 20.
	• Find prime factors.
	• Investigate products of odd or even numbers.
	• Make general statements about odd or even numbers, and give examples.
	• Solve number puzzles and explain methods and reasoning.
Overview	• Recognise and use multiples.
	• Recognise and use prime numbers.
	• Write a number as the product of prime factors.
	• Make general statements about the products of odd and even numbers.

How you could plan this unit

	Stage 1	Stage 2	Stage 3	Stage 4	Stage 5
Content and vocabulary	Using multiples *multiples, common multiples, digital roots, pattern*	Recognising prime numbers *multiples, prime numbers*	Finding prime factors *prime numbers, factor, prime factors, factor tree*	Investigating products of odd and even numbers *product, odd numbers, even numbers, general statement, general tables*	
Notes		Resource page A			

Using multiples

We are going to work with multiples

**Oral/mental starter
p 173**

Whole-class work

- Ask the children to help you build a multiples grid on the board, as shown.

- Invite the children to say each sequence and to extend each sequence before they make a mistake.

- Discuss the properties of each count-on sequence, such as: odd and even numbers, patterns in the unit digits, patterns in the digital roots (the sum of the digits until a single digit is reached), how many numbers have single digits, have a 1, 2, 3, and so on to 10 digit.

Count in **2s**	2	4	6	8	10	12	14	16	18	20
Count in **3s**	3	6	9	12	15	18	21	24	27	30
Count in **4s**	4	8	12	16	20	24	28	32	36	40
Count in **5s**	5	10	15	20	25	30	35	40	45	50
Count in **6s**	6	12	18	24	30	36	42	48	54	60
Count in **7s**	7	14	21	28	35	42	49	56	63	70
Count in **8s**	8	16	24	32	40	48	56	64	72	80
Count in **9s**	9	18	27	36	45	54	63	72	81	90
Count in **10s**	10	20	30	40	50	60	70	80	90	100

- Point to the count-in-twos sequence. Remind the children that each number is a multiple of 2.

- *Why is each number a multiple of 2?*

- Repeat for the other sequences, in turn.

- Ask questions about multiples, some suggestions are given below.

- *Of which numbers is 10 a multiple? Of how many numbers is 8 a multiple?*

- *Which numbers are multiples of only one number?*

- *Which numbers do not appear in any of the sequences? Are these numbers multiples of any number?*

- *Find multiples of numbers whose sum of digits is 9. Of which numbers are they multiples?*

Independent, paired or group work

- Ask the children, with help from the grid on the board, to complete sorting diagrams as shown below for as many numbers as they can.

	Multiples of 4	Not multiples of 4
Multiples of 5		
Not multiples of 5		

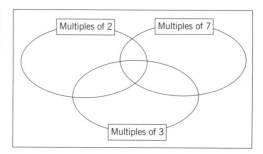

Plenary

- Draw on the board some larger versions of the sorting diagrams. Ask the children for numbers that belong in each region.

- Record them. Discuss common multiples.

Recognising prime numbers

Advance Organiser

We are going to find prime numbers

Oral/mental starter
p 173

You will need: calculators (one per child), resource page A (one per child and one enlarged)

Whole-class work

- Write this set of numbers on the board: *2 3 5 7 11 13 17 19 23 29 31.*

- Explain that you have written a set of numbers on the board that is in order, but there is no rule for the sequence.

- *What are these numbers called?*

- Explain that the numbers are called prime numbers.

- *What is special about a prime number?*

- Explain that a prime number is divisible by only two numbers, 1 and itself.

- *Tell me the next prime number.*

- Test any number that is suggested by dividing it by 2, 3, 5, 7, 11, and so on.

- Explain or draw out that there is no need to test for divisibility by 4, as any number that is divisible by 4 is also divisible by 2. The same argument applies to other numbers that have factors other than 1 and themselves.

- Show the children an enlarged top half of resource page A.

- Ask them to tell you the prime numbers from 2 to 31 to shade in.

- *The number 2 is an even prime number. Can you think of another even number that is prime?*

1	2	3	4	5	6	7	8	9	10
11	12	13	14	15	16	17	18	19	20
21	22	23	24	25	26	27	28	29	30
31	32	33	34	35	36	37	38	39	40
41	42	43	44	45	46	47	48	49	50

- Explain that no other even number is a prime because primes are only divisible by 1 and themselves and even numbers are always divisible by 2.

Independent, paired or group work

- Ask the children to complete resource page A. You may wish to allow them to use a calculator to test each number for divisibility.

Plenary

- Use the enlarged 1 to 100 square from resource page A and ask the class to help you shade the remaining prime numbers up to 100.

- Ask the children to test the numbers, either mentally or with a calculator.

- Invite the children to tell you how to write numbers as the sum of two prime numbers.

Name: _____

Finding prime numbers

Colour every multiple of 2 after 2.
Do the same for multiples of 3, 5 and 7.

Colour the prime numbers.

1	2	3	4	5	6	7	8	9	10
11	12	13	14	15	16	17	18	19	20
21	22	23	24	25	26	27	28	29	30
31	32	33	34	35	36	37	38	39	40
41	42	43	44	45	46	47	48	49	50
51	52	53	54	55	56	57	58	59	60
61	62	63	64	65	66	67	68	69	70
71	72	73	74	75	76	77	78	79	80
81	82	83	84	85	86	87	88	89	90
91	92	93	94	95	96	97	98	99	100

1	2	3	4	5	6	7	8	9	10
11	12	13	14	15	16	17	18	19	20
21	22	23	24	25	26	27	28	29	30
31	32	33	34	35	36	37	38	39	40
41	42	43	44	45	46	47	48	49	50
51	52	53	54	55	56	57	58	59	60
61	62	63	64	65	66	67	68	69	70
71	72	73	74	75	76	77	78	79	80
81	82	83	84	85	86	87	88	89	90
91	92	93	94	95	96	97	98	99	100

Prime numbers that have a difference of 2 are called twin primes. 3 and 5 are twin primes.
Write all the twin primes up to 100.

☐ and ☐   ☐ and ☐   ☐ and ☐   ☐ and ☐   ☐ and ☐

☐ and ☐   ☐ and ☐   ☐ and ☐   ☐ and ☐

Write as many numbers as you can that are the sum of two prime numbers.

Number	Sum of two primes	Number	Sum of two primes	Number	Sum of two primes
1		11		21	
2		12		22	
3		13		23	
4		14		24	
5	2 + 3	15		25	
6		16		26	
7	2 + 5	17		27	
8		18		28	
9		19		29	
10		20		30	

Classworks © Classworks Numeracy author team, Nelson Thornes Ltd, 2003

Finding prime factors

Oral/mental starter
p 173

Advance Organiser

We are going to find prime factors

Whole-class work

- Draw on the board an empty factor tree similar to the one shown. Tell the children that you are going to use this diagram to find the prime factors of a number.

- Write the number 6 in the top circle.

- *Is 6 a prime number? How did you decide?*
  What numbers is 6 divisible by?

- Write this number sentence on the board: 6 = 2 × 3.

- *Are 2 and 3 prime numbers?*

- Explain that as 2 and 3 are prime numbers, we write them in the two circles to show that the prime factors of 6 are 2 and 3.

- Repeat the activity for 10, 15 and 9.

- Draw on the board a new (empty) factor tree similar to the one shown. Write in *30*.

- *Is 30 a prime number? How did you decide? What numbers is 30 divisible by?*

- Write on the board: *30 = 2 × 15.*

- Write 2 and 15 in the diagram.

- *Is 2 a prime number? Is 15 a prime number? What is 15 divisible by?*

- Extend the diagram to show that *30 = 2 × 15* and that *30 = 2 × 3 × 5.*

- Explain that as the factors in the bottom row are prime factors, the diagram does not go any further.

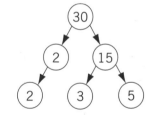

- Point out that the 2 is written again in the bottom row so that all three prime factors can be seen across the row.

Independent, paired or group work

- Ask the children to write similar factor trees for 22, 26, 14, 21, 33, 35, 39, 51, 12, 42 and 45.

Plenary

- Choose some examples from the factor trees the children have drawn to work on together.

- Ask the children to discuss how they worked out each tree.

- Ask the children what number will be at the top of a factor tree that has 2, 3, 5 and 7 along the bottom row.

Investigating products of odd and even numbers

Advance Organiser

We are going to investigate odd and even numbers

Whole-class work

- Draw on the board the two general tables, as shown, about the sum and difference of odd and even numbers without the 'answers' – that is, with just the column and row headings.

+	Odd	Even
Odd	Even	Odd
Even	Odd	Even

−	Odd	Even
Odd	Even	Odd
Even	Odd	Even

- Remind the children of what the tables are expressing.

- *What is the sum of an odd number and an odd number?*

- Ask for examples to support the general statement.

- Record each example on the board.

- Write 'even' in the table to show that odd + odd = even.

- Repeat the activity for the sums of odd and even, even and odd, even and even.

- Do the same for the difference table.

×	Odd	Even
Odd		
Even		

- Draw on the board a general table for the product of odd and even numbers as shown.

- Write on the board as shown.

- Ask the children to predict which is correct, odd or even. Take a vote on which answer is correct. Record the vote on the board. Discuss and record examples of odd × odd multiplications.

$$\text{Odd} \times \text{Odd} = \begin{array}{l} \text{Even} \\ \text{Odd} \end{array}$$

Independent, paired or group work

- Ask the children to investigate the problem by choosing six pairs of numbers and recording their products for each section of the product table; that is, six pairs of odd × odd, six pairs of odd × even, and six pairs of even × even. They then should complete the table.

Plenary

- Complete the general table for the products of odd and even numbers using the children's supporting examples.

- Write the three general statements about products of odd and even numbers on the board, such as *the product of an odd number and an even number is an even number.*

Properties of Number (5)

Outcome

Children will be able to use different techniques to estimate and approximate

Medium-term plan objectives	• Consolidate all previous work. • Use the vocabulary of estimation and approximation. • Consolidate rounding an integer to the nearest 10, 100 or 1000. • Develop calculator skills and use a calculator effectively.
Overview	• Estimate the position of a number on an undivided number line. • Find approximations using rounding.

How you could plan this unit

	Stage 1	Stage 2	Stage 3	Stage 4	Stage 5
Content and vocabulary	Estimating numbers on a number line *approximate, estimate, number line*	Using rounding to find approximations *approximation, round to nearest 100, 10 or unit*			
Notes	Resource page A				

Estimating numbers on a number line

Advance Organiser

We are going to find numbers on a number line

Oral/mental starter p 173

You will need: resource page A (one per child)

Whole-class work

- Draw an unmarked number line on the board. Write in the numbers *0* and *10 000*.

- Establish that the children understand that 0 and 10 000 are positions on the line and that there are numbers between 0 and 10 000.
- *What do the arrowheads indicate at each end of the number line?*
- Draw an arrow at approximately 6000.

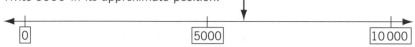

- *What multiple of 1000 is the arrow pointing to?*
- Discuss how the children decided.
- Explain that when making estimates of numbers on a number line, finding the 'middle' number is helpful.
- Invite a child to point to the position of the middle number.
- *What number is Evan pointing to? How did you work it out?*
- Write *5000* in its approximate position.

- Ask the children how this helps them decide where the arrow is pointing. Agree it is roughly at 6000.
- Erase the arrow and draw arrows at other multiples of 1000 and multiples of 500 positions.
- Repeat the activity with a 0 to 0.1 number line. In this case you may wish to encourage children to mark the approximate positions of the multiples of 0.01 to help them estimate the number the arrow is pointing to.

Independent, paired or group work

- Ask the children to complete resource page A.

Plenary

- Go through the children's answers to resource page A, discussing the different methods used.

PUPIL PAGE

Name: _____

Estimating positions on a number line

Write in the numbers the arrows are pointing to.

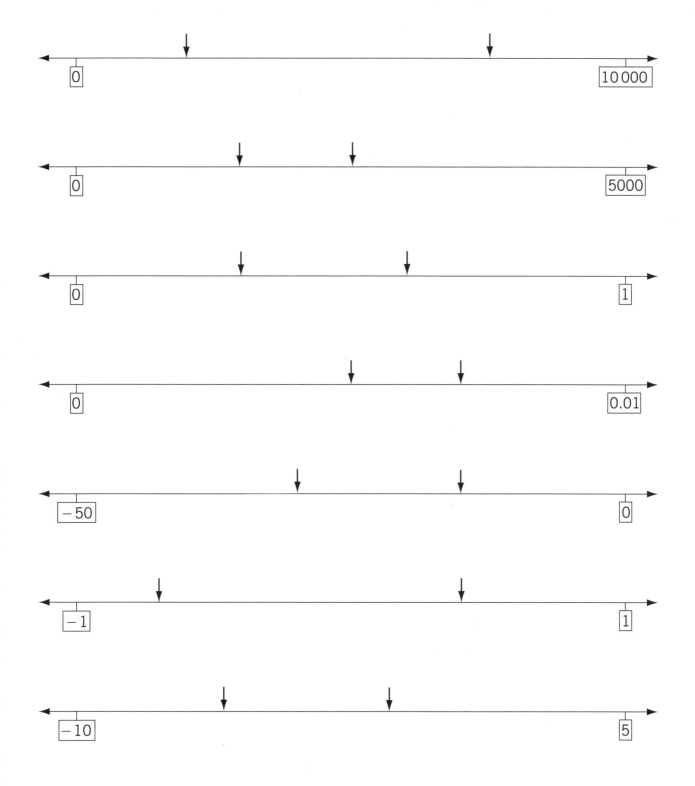

Using rounding to find approximations

Oral/mental starter p 173

Advance Organiser

We are going to find approximate answers to calculations

You will need: calculators (one per child)

Whole-class work

- Write this addition on the board: *37.6 + 51.9*.
- *What is a good approximation for 37.6 + 51.9?*
- Discuss the children's different methods.
- Draw on the board the first rounding diagram, as shown, but without the answers.
- Explain that we can find approximations to calculations by rounding the numbers.
- *What is 37.6 rounded to the nearest 10?*
- Record *40* on the diagram. Repeat for 51.9. Record the answer, as shown.
- *What is another approximation for 37.6 + 51.9?*
- Repeat the activity for rounding to the nearest unit.

- The children will notice that in this example the approximate answers are the same for each rounding. Warn them that this is not always the case.

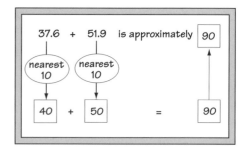

- Everyone now uses their calculator to find the exact answer to 37.6 + 51.9.

- Repeat for an addition for which the two different ways of rounding give different approximations; for example, 34.8 + 51.6.

- Discuss situations when each type of rounding is most appropriate – whether accuracy or speed is important in a given context.

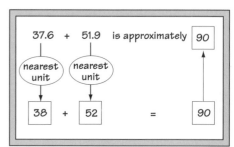

Independent, paired or group work

- Ask the children to use a similar approach to approximate other decimal calculations; for example, 146.2 + 284.1, 712.4 – 503.6, 8.82 × 5.19, 36.48 ÷ 4.8.
- They can use a variety of methods to approximate, then find the answer, to the following as well: 92.73 + 87.69, 145.3 – 62.71, 75.4 × 8.3, 61.64 ÷ 6.7.

Plenary

- Invite the children to explain how they worked out some of the examples above.
- Discuss differences or similarities in approximate answers depending on the rounding.

Properties of Number (6)

Outcome

Children will be able to investigate and solve number puzzles

Medium-term plan objectives

- Factorise numbers to 100 into prime factors.
- Investigate number sequences.
- Develop a generalised relationship in words; express it in a formula using symbols.
- Solve number puzzles and explain methods and reasoning.

Overview

- Factorise a number into prime factors.
- Investigate digital roots of count-on sequences.
- Solve an Arithmogon puzzle.

How you could plan this unit

	Stage 1	Stage 2	Stage 3	Stage 4	Stage 5
Content and vocabulary	Factorising numbers into their prime factors *factor tree, prime numbers, prime factors*	Investigating count-on sequences *digital roots*	Solving number puzzles *Arithmogon*		
Notes	Resource page A		Resource page B		

Factorising numbers into their prime factors

Advance Organiser

We are going to find prime factors

Oral/mental starter p 173

You will need: calculators (one per child), resource page A (one per child)

Whole-class work

- Remind the children what is special about a prime number.

- *Write all the prime numbers less than 30.*

- Collect the list of prime numbers from the children and record them on the board:
  2 3 5 7 11 13 17 19 23 29.

- Draw a blank factor tree on the board, as shown.

- Remind them what a factor tree is and what it does. Use a simple example, if necessary.

- Write in the bottom row the prime numbers *2, 2, 3* and *3*.

- *Which number when factorised into prime numbers produces 2, 2, 3 and 3?*

- Discuss the different methods the children used to find the answer.

- Show them how to work backwards on the factor tree to find the number that has the prime factors 2, 2, 3 and 3.

- Complete the factor tree. Record on the board as shown how 36 can be written as a product of its prime factors.

  $36 = 2 \times 2 \times 3 \times 3$

  $\quad = 2^2 \times 3^2$

- Discuss the writing of the factors as square numbers.

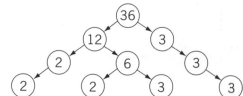

Independent, paired or group work

- Ask the children to complete resource page A.

Plenary

- Choose some of the children's examples from resource page A to show the making of a number when given its prime factors.

- Work through the last two examples on resource page A on the board.

Name: _____

Finding prime numbers

These are the prime numbers less than 30:

2   3   5   7   11   13   17   19   23   29

Choose four prime numbers (you may repeat a number if you wish) to complete the bottom row of each factor tree. Complete the factor tree.

Write the number as a product of its prime factors. Use square number notation where appropriate.

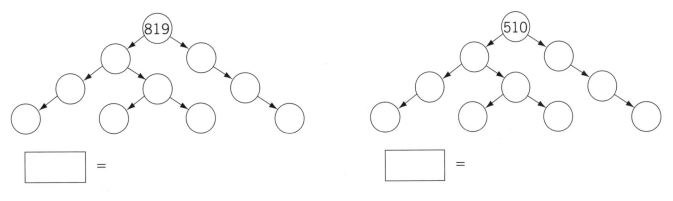

Complete each factor tree. Write each number as the product of its prime factors.
Use a calculator to help you.

Investigating count-on sequences

Oral/mental starter
p 173

Advance Organiser

We are going to find patterns in count-on sequences

Whole-class work

- Explain to the children that you have a hidden rule and that they have to work in pairs to guess what it is.

- Draw on the board, step-by-step, the digital root diagram for 469.

  469 ──► 19 ──► 10 ──► 1

- At each step ask: *What is my rule? How did I know which number to write next? What do you notice about the digits each time?*

- Explain, if no one points it out, that to find the digital root, you first add the digits of your number together (4 + 6 + 9 = 19). If this is not a single-digit number, you add the digits again (1 + 9 = 10) and continue in this way until you arrive at a single digit (1 + 0 = 1). This is the digital root of the number. Stress that the last number must always be a single digit.

- Write these numbers on the board: *5673* and *18,497*. Ask the children to find the digital root of each number.

- Show how to find the digital roots of the two numbers.

  5673 ──► 21 ──► 3

  18497 ──► 29 ──► 11 ──► 2

- Write on the board the count-in-threes sequence that starts at 3.

- On the board draw a large digital root circle. Show the children how to draw the digital root diagram for the count-in-threes sequence.

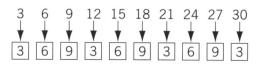

Count on in 3s

- Emphasise the direction of each line on the diagram as this shows the order of the pattern.

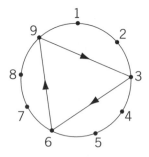

Independent, paired or group work

- Ask the children to find the digital root pattern for each sequence from counting on in ones to counting on in nines and draw root circles for each. (They must have accurately marked circles for the diagrams to work.)

Plenary

- Ask the children to describe each root circle in turn. Compare the diagrams on the board. Ask the children to point out similarities and differences; for example, count in threes is the same as count in sixes, but in the opposite direction.

Solving number puzzles

Advance Organiser

We are going to solve a mathematical puzzle

Oral/mental starter p 173

You will need: resource page B (one per child)

Whole-class work

- Draw on the board a square Arithmogon as shown with the numbers 5, 8, 7 and 9 in the circles.

- Explain the rule that the number in a box is the sum of the numbers in the two adjacent or joining circles.

- Together, complete the numbers in the boxes.

- Erase all the numbers and write in the boxes the numbers 6, 5, 3 and 4.

- Explain that the rule is the same.

- *Find the numbers in the circles that add to make the number in the box between the circles.*

- Collect the different solutions that the children find. There is an infinite number of solutions, so it is best to restrict them to whole numbers. In this case there are four solutions.

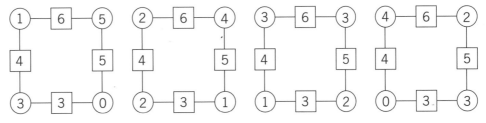

- Discuss strategies that the children used. Explain that a good strategy is to be systematic, starting with the smallest whole number.

- You may wish to challenge some children to find solutions that involve negative numbers, decimals or fractions.

Independent, paired or group work

- Ask the children to complete resource page B.

Plenary

- Discuss the different solutions that the children find for each of the first two Arithmogons. The final one does not have any solutions. Ask the children what is special about the four numbers in the first two examples that is not true of the third one. You may give them a clue by suggesting they look at pairs of numbers.

- Square Arithmogons only have solutions when the sum of opposite pairs is equal. When this is true there is an infinite number of solutions.

Name: _____

Solving puzzles

Find four different solutions of the Arithmogon puzzle.

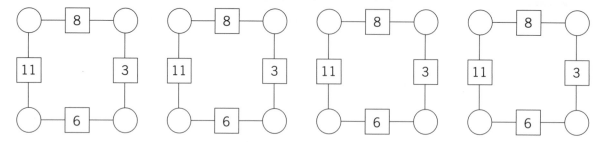

Find eight different multiple-of-10 solutions of the Arithmogon puzzle.

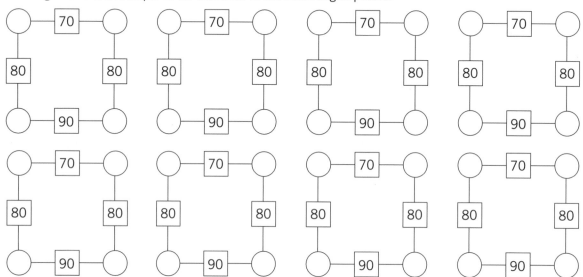

Can you be the first to find a solution of this Arithmogon puzzle? Draw your own diagrams if needed.

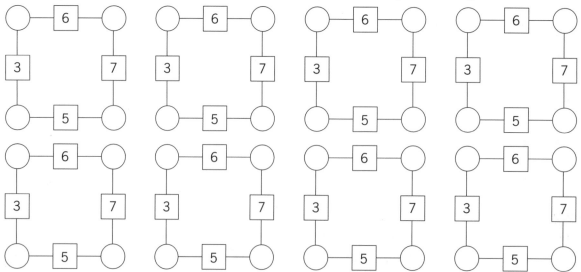

Classworks © Classworks Numeracy author team, Nelson Thornes Ltd, 2003

Addition and Subtraction (1)

Outcome

Children will be able to use jottings to support addition and subtraction of large numbers and decimals

Medium-term plan objectives	• Consolidate all previous work.
	• Find a difference by counting up.
	• Add or subtract a multiple of 10, 100, 1000, and adjust.
	• If appropriate, use pencil and paper methods.
	• Extend written methods to column addition and subtraction of numbers involving decimals.

Overview	• Find differences by counting on in multiples of 1, 10, 100 and 1000.
	• Add a near single-digit number, and adjust.
	• Subtract a near single-digit number, and adjust.

How you could plan this unit

	Stage 1	Stage 2	Stage 3	Stage 4	Stage 5
Content and vocabulary	Finding the difference by counting on	Adding a near-multiple of a whole number	Subtracting a near-multiple of a whole number		
	count on, multiples of 10, 100, 1000, difference, subtraction	near-multiple of a whole number	near-multiple of a whole number		
Notes			Resource page A		

Finding the difference by counting on

Oral/mental starter p 174

Advance Organiser

We are going to subtract four-digit numbers by counting on

Whole-class work

- Write this subtraction on the board: *7000 – 3562*.

- *Work out the answer to 7000 – 3562.*

- Discuss the different methods that the children used and what they thought about each method.

- Use the diagram to show them how to count up in multiples of 1, 10, 100 and 1000 to find the answer.

- Emphasise how to count up to the next multiple of 10, then the next multiple of 100, then the next multiple of 1000 and finally count on in multiples of 1000.

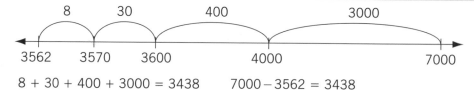

$8 + 30 + 400 + 3000 = 3438$ $7000 - 3562 = 3438$

- Explain that the aim is to develop a mental approach and that drawing a number line is helpful, but it takes time.

- *Work in pairs to make a simpler diagram for the same subtraction.*

- Discuss the different diagrams that pairs develop.

- Draw from everyone's efforts and talk through the stages of calculation. Show them the diagram below as representation of the same process.

$$3562 \xrightarrow{+8} 3570 \xrightarrow{+30} 3600 \xrightarrow{+400} 4000 \xrightarrow{+3000} 7000$$

- Discuss in what ways the diagram is simpler than the number line method.

- *Work out the subtraction 5000 – 1786 using a diagram like this.*

Independent, paired or group work

- Give the children further problems to solve, for example, 9000 – 4263, 4000 – 2116, 8000 – 5647, 8000 – 4529, using either method, or another that they find easier. They must record what they do each time. Provide examples of how to use the second method outlined above, as shown.

$$1874 \xrightarrow{\square} 1880 \xrightarrow{\square} 1900 \xrightarrow{\square} 2000 \xrightarrow{\square} 3000$$

$$3000 - 1874 = \square$$

Plenary

- Choose examples of different methods of recording and ask some children to repeat them on the board. Ask other children to describe what they think is happening at each stage.

Adding a near-multiple of a whole number

Oral/mental starter
p 174

Advance Organiser

We are going to add decimal numbers

Whole-class work

- Write this addition on the board: *7.6 + 0.9.*

- Discuss the value of each digit in the two numbers.

- *What is the answer to 7.6 add 0.9?*

- Discuss the different methods the children used.

- Explain that you are going to show them a method that works for all numbers that have nine-tenths or a nine in the tenths position.

- Build the diagram, step-by-step, making sure the children understand that the calculations in each line have the same answer.

- *Why have I changed 0.9 into 1 − 0.1?*

- At the side of the diagram, write the same method in symbols.

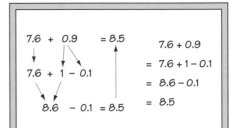

- As you are doing this, relate each step to the same step in the diagram.

- Point out the use of the equals sign at the start of each row. Ask the children to explain why this is necessary and what it means about the relationship between the calculations in each row.

- Repeat the activity with the addition 4.7 + 2.9.

Independent, paired or group work

- Ask the children to draw similar diagrams to help them to solve 6.5 + 0.9, 8.4 + 5.9, 5.8 + 3.9, 9.3 + 4.9. They can use any method they choose to solve 3.6 + 1.9, 2.9 + 6.9, 8.6 + 7.9, but they must be able to describe afterwards what they did.

- Finally, ask them to use the digits 5, 8 and 2 to complete each of the following additions in a different way, then find the answers.

$$\Box . \Box + \Box . 9 = \qquad \Box . \Box + \Box . 9 = \qquad \Box . \Box + \Box . 9 =$$

$$\Box . \Box + \Box . 9 = \qquad \Box . \Box + \Box . 9 = \qquad \Box . \Box + \Box . 9 =$$

Plenary

- Invite the children to show how they worked out one of the examples above. Allow them to choose which example to use. They should describe their method. Ask for alternatives and encourage the children to discuss differences or similarities between them.

Subtracting a near-multiple of a whole number

Oral/mental starter
p 174

Advance Organiser

We are going to subtract decimal numbers

You will need: resource page A (one per child)

Whole-class work

- Write this subtraction on the board: *8.3 – 0.9*.

- Discuss the value of each digit in the two numbers.

- *What is the answer to 8.3 – 0.9?*

- Discuss the different methods the children used.

- Explain that you are going to show them a method that works for all numbers that have nine-tenths or a nine in the tenths position. Remind them that they used a similar method for adding such decimal numbers.

- Build up the diagram, step-by-step, making sure the children understand that the calculations in each line have the same answer.

- At the side of the diagram, write the same method in symbols.

- As you are doing this, relate each step to the same step in the diagram.

- Some children may have difficulty understanding that instead of taking away 0.9, they are taking away 1 and adding 0.1. Use a number line to explain this if necessary.

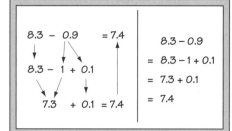

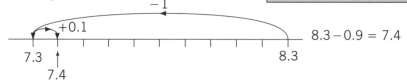

- Point out the use of the equals sign at the start of each row. Ask the children to explain why this is necessary and what it means about the relationship between the calculations in each row.

- Repeat the activity with the subtraction 6.4 – 3.9.

Independent, paired or group work

- Ask the children to complete resource page A.

Plenary

- Invite the children to show how they worked out one of the examples on resource page A. Allow them to choose which example to use.

- Discuss any different methods or answers.

Name: _____

Subtracting decimal numbers

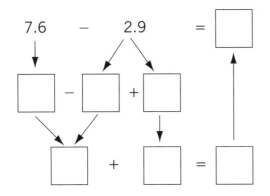

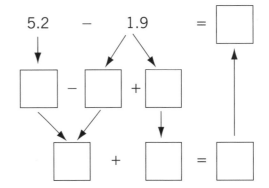

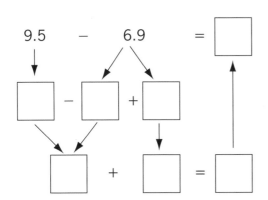

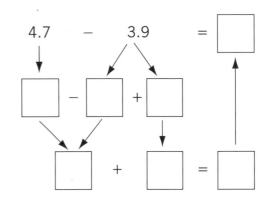

Use any method to find the answers to these subtractions:

$8.8 - 6.9 =$ $7.1 - 5.9 =$ $3.6 - 1.9 =$

Use three of the digits 4, 9, 2 and 7 to complete each subtraction in a different way.
Make sure the first number is larger than the second. Find the answers.

☐ . ☐ − ☐ . 9 =   ☐ . ☐ − ☐ . 9 =

☐ . ☐ − ☐ . 9 =   ☐ . ☐ − ☐ . 9 =

☐ . ☐ − ☐ . 9 =   ☐ . ☐ − ☐ . 9 =

Addition and Subtraction (2)

Outcome

Children will be able to investigate addition and subtraction puzzles and use different methods to calculate answers

Medium-term plan objectives	
	● Consolidate all previous work.
	● Extend written methods to column addition and subtraction of numbers involving decimals.

Overview	
	● Add three-digit and four-digit near-doubles.
	● Make three-digit additions and the corresponding subtractions.
	● Add three or more multiples of 1000.

How you could plan this unit

	Stage 1	Stage 2	Stage 3	Stage 4	Stage 5
Content and vocabulary	Adding near-doubles *near-double*	Relating additions to subtractions *digits, sorting*	Adding three or more multiples of 1000 *multiple of 1000, predict*	Written methods involving decimals	
Notes		Resource page A		Talk the children through a column addition method involving decimal numbers, asking them to describe, in their own words, what happens at each stage.	

Adding near-doubles

Advance Organiser

We are going to add near-doubles

Oral/mental starter p 174

Whole-class work

- Write on the board: *395 + 412*.

- *What is the answer to 395 + 412? If you can, work out the answer mentally.*

- Discuss the different methods the children used. Ask the children to look again at the two numbers in the addition.

- *What is the number that both numbers are near?* Explain that we can use the fact that both numbers are near 400 to use a double to work out the answer. Invite a child to show how this might be done.

- Build on the board the near-double addition as shown, step-by-step, in symbols.

- Ask why the equals sign is at the start of each line. Make sure the children understand that the calculations in each line have the same answer.

- Emphasise the importance of setting out working systematically.

- Repeat the activity with the addition 7608 + 7484. Again, build up the addition step-by-step.

$$395 + 412$$
$$= 400 - 5 + 400 + 12$$
$$= 400 + 400 - 5 + 12$$
$$= 800 + 7$$
$$= 807$$

$$7608 + 7484$$
$$= 7500 + 108 + 7500 - 16$$
$$= 7500 + 7500 + 108 - 16$$
$$= 15000 + 92$$
$$= 15092$$

Independent, paired or group work

- Ask the children to use a similar method to find answers to 609 + 581, 853 + 842, 521 + 487, 4026 + 3984, 2402 + 2661, 3705 + 3300. Ask them to show their working each time.

- Then ask them to use the digits 6, 2, 9 and 5 to complete the following addition in different ways. They should investigate finding the smallest and largest possible answers.

| 4 | 5 | | | + | 4 | 6 | | | = |

Plenary

- Together, look at some of the examples that the children made with the four digits in the last investigation.

- Record as many different additions as you can from the children.

- Discuss what methods you could use to solve each one, and why they might be different each time, or why some children prefer particular methods to others.

Relating additions to subtractions

Advance Organiser

We are going to make three-digit additions

You will need: resource page A (one per child and one enlarged)

Whole-class work

- Write on the board the digits 1 to 9 and the blank three-digit addition as shown.

$$\boxed{}\boxed{}\boxed{} + \boxed{}\boxed{}\boxed{} = \boxed{}\boxed{}\boxed{}$$

- *I am trying to use as many of the nine digits as I can to complete the addition.*

- Write in *521 + 468. How many different digits are in this addition? What is the answer to 521 + 468?*

- Complete the addition. *How many different digits are in 521 + 468 = 989?* Point out that 8 and 9 are used twice each, so that only 7 different digits appear in the addition.

$$\boxed{5}\boxed{2}\boxed{1} + \boxed{4}\boxed{6}\boxed{8} = \boxed{9}\boxed{8}\boxed{9}$$

- Show the children the enlarged addition sorting table from resource page A. Ask the children to help you write the addition in the correct column.

Additions

Use 6 digits	Use 7 digits	Use 8 digits	Use 9 digits
	521 + 468 = 989		

- Ask the children to make a copy of the blank addition.

- *Here is your challenge. Use as many of the digits 1 to 9 as you can to complete the addition. Can you use more than seven different digits in one addition?*

- Ask the children for their addition and where to sort it in the grid.

Independent, paired or group work

- Ask the children to complete resource page A. When they have sorted their nine numbers in the addition grid, explain that for each addition they can make a subtraction that uses the same numbers.

- Ask them to make a subtraction for each addition and sort it in the subtraction grid.

Plenary

- Collect and record additions and corresponding subtractions for sorting in to the two grids.

- Ask if anyone has managed to use all nine digits in an addition, for example, 173 + 286 = 459.

PUPIL PAGE

Name: _____

Additions and subtractions

Use as many of the digits 1 to 9 as you can to complete each addition.

| 1 | 2 | 3 | + | 4 | 5 | 6 | = | 5 | 7 | 9 |

Sort each addition in the sorting grid.

Additions

Use 6 digits	Use 7 digits	Use 8 digits	Use 9 digits
		123 + 456 = 579	

Make a subtraction for each addition. Sort them into the grid below.

Subtractions

Use 6 digits	Use 7 digits	Use 8 digits	Use 9 digits
		579 − 123 = 456	

Classworks © Classworks Numeracy author team, Nelson Thornes Ltd, 2003

Adding three or more multiples of 1000

Advance Organiser

We are going to add multiples of 1000

Oral/mental starter p 174

Whole-class work

- Write this addition on the board: *3000 + 8000 + 6000 + 7000.*

- *What is the answer to this addition?*

- Discuss the different methods the children used. Write on the board the following pattern of related facts after re-ordering the numbers to make a pair that make 10.

- Ask the children to copy the additions and to write the next two lines in the pattern. Do the same for 9000 + 2000 + 1000 + 7000.

> $3 + 7 + 8 + 6 = 24$
>
> $30 + 70 + 80 + 60 = 240$
>
> $300 + 700 + 800 + 600 = 2400$
>
> $3000 + 7000 + 8000 + 6000 = 24\,000$

- Extend the idea to additions of five and then six numbers; for example, 6000 + 5000 + 8000 + 5000 + 4000, then 1000 + 7000 + 9000 + 4000 + 6000 + 3000.

Independent, paired or group work

- Ask the children to investigate finding additions of three 'thousands' numbers that total 3000, 4000, 5000, 6000, 7000, 8000 and 9000. Encourage them to work systematically. Examples of what the additions should look like are shown below.

  1000 + 1000 + 1000 = 3000
  2000 + 1000 + 1000 = 4000
  1000 + 2000 + 1000 = 4000
  1000 + 1000 + 2000 = 4000

Plenary

- Draw on the board the blank table, as shown, with the row and column headings but not the numbers of additions written in.

- Explain the table. Collect information from the children about how many additions it is possible to make for each total. It will be necessary to agree on when two additions are the same. The simplest is to say that two additions that use the same three numbers are the same.

Total	3000	4000	5000	6000	7000	8000	9000
Number of additions	1	1	2	2	3	3	4

- Complete the table. Discuss any patterns that appear.

- Ask the children to predict how many different additions they think there are that have a total of 10 000, 11 000 and so on. They could test their predictions.

Addition and Subtraction (3)

Outcome

Children will be able to use mental and written techniques to solve decimal additions, and additions and subtractions of large numbers

Medium-term plan objectives

- Use number facts and place-value to add and subtract mentally.
- Extend written methods to column addition and subtraction of numbers involving decimals.

Overview

- Add and subtract four-digit multiples of 100.
- Find the number that added to a two-place decimal makes the next higher integer.
- Add two or more decimal numbers.

How you could plan this unit

	Stage 1	Stage 2	Stage 3	Stage 4	Stage 5
Content and vocabulary	Adding or subtracting four-digit multiples of 100 *pattern*	Counting on to make a decimal up to the next whole number	Adding decimal numbers *units, tenths, hundredths*		
Notes		Resource page A			

43

Adding or subtracting four-digit multiples of 100

Advance Organiser

We are going to add and subtract multiples of 100

Oral/mental starter p 174

Whole-class work

- Write this subtraction on the board: *4300 – 1700.*

- *What is the answer to this subtraction?*

- Discuss the different methods the children used. Write on the board the pattern of related facts as shown.

- Ask the children to copy and complete the subtractions and to write the next two lines in the pattern.

$$43 - 17 =$$
$$430 - 170 =$$
$$4300 - 1700 =$$

- Discuss how the pattern helps find the answer to questions with larger numbers. Do the same for *7200 – 2600.*

- Write this addition on the board: *3600 + 2500.*

- *What is the answer to this addition?*

- Discuss the different methods the children used. Write on the board the pattern of related facts as shown.

- Ask the children to copy and complete the additions and to write the next two lines in the pattern.

$$36 + 25 = 61$$
$$360 + 250 = 610$$
$$3600 + 2500 = 6100$$

- Discuss how the pattern helps find the answer to questions with larger numbers. Do the same for *6700 + 1900.*

Independent, paired or group work

- Ask the children to investigate similar patterns as shown. They should complete the calculations and add two more lines to the pattern.

43 + 38 =	54 + 47 =	65 – 48 =	84 – 39 =
430 + 380 =	540 + 470 =	650 – 480 =	840 – 390 =
4300 + 3800 =	5400 + 4700 =	6500 – 4800 =	8400 – 3900 =

- Then ask them to calculate 2900 + 6400 and 5600 – 2700, and show their method.

- They can then identify the missing digits, to make the following calculations correct:

	5		+		7	0	0	=		2	0	0
	8	0	+	2			0	=		4		0
	7		0	–	5	8			=	3		0	0
3		0	0	–		9	0		=		2		0

Plenary

- Choose examples from each section of the children's work. Invite them to explain how they worked out the solutions.

- Discuss different methods and answers each time.

Counting on to make a decimal up to the next whole number

Oral/mental starter
p 174

Advance Organiser

We are going to solve missing number problems

You will need: resource page A (one per child)

Whole-class work

- Write the following problem on the board: *I am thinking of the number 3.72. I add another number to it. My answer is 4. What is the other number?*

- Read out the problem. Ask the children to solve the problem. Discuss the methods they used. Show them how to write the problem in symbols.

  $3.72 + \boxed{} = 4$

- Establish that the children understand the value of each digit in the numbers.

- Explain how a number line can help to find the missing number.

  $0.08 + 0.2 = 0.28$

- Build the number line step by step asking the children to explain each step and the reasons for it.

- You will constantly need to remind the children of the value of digits as you work with the numbers and the jumps.

- Ask the children to make a simpler diagram than the number line that solves the same problem.

- Discuss the children's different diagrams. Show them the diagram below.

  $3.72 \xrightarrow{+\ 0.08} 3.8 \xrightarrow{+\ 0.2} 4$

- Repeat the activity with the problem: *I am thinking of the number 5.64. I add another number to it. My answer is 6. What is the other number?*

Independent, paired or group work

- Ask the children to complete resource page A.

Plenary

- Work through some examples on resource page A.

- Discuss different methods and answers. Encourage the children to describe each stage of a calculation in detail and to write their methods on the board.

Name: _____

Finding missing numbers

Find the missing jumps.

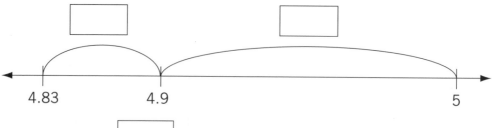

What added to 4.83 makes 5? ☐

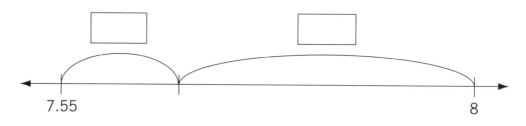

What added to 7.55 makes 8? ☐

Complete each diagram:

What added to 8.76 makes 9? ☐

What added to 2.68 makes 3? ☐

Solve the problems:

I am thinking of 6.47. I add another number to it. My answer is 7. What is the other number?

I am thinking of 9.31. I add another number to it. My answer is 10. What is the other number?

I am thinking of 1.25. I add another number to it. My answer is 2. What is the other number?

Classworks © Classworks Numeracy author team, Nelson Thornes Ltd, 2003

Adding decimal numbers

Advance Organiser

We are going to add decimal numbers

**Oral/mental starter
p 174**

Whole-class work

- Write this addition on the board: *0.6 + 0.08*. Discuss the different values of the digits in the two numbers.

- *Find the answer to 0.6 + 0.08. Explain how you did it.*

- Discuss the different methods the children used. Explain that with decimal numbers it helps to see the numbers written in columns in a place-value grid. Draw a blank grid on the board as shown.

- In turn, point to the heading of each column.

- *What does this letter stand for? How many tenths make one unit? How many hundredths make one tenth?*

- Invite the children to write the numbers in the grid to represent the addition in column form.

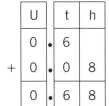

- Remind them of the importance of keeping the digits in the correct columns, and the decimal points below each other.

- *What is the sum of 0.6 and 0.08?* Ask the children to explain how they did it.

- Repeat the activity with the additions 1.71 + 2.38, 0.85 + 4.2, 6.9 + 7.64, using columns, then follow by calculating the same examples without using the column diagram.

Independent, paired or group work

- Ask the children to draw similar diagrams to help them solve 0.38 + 5.9, 7.6 + 1.52, 3.75 + 2.86, 4.7 + 0.64, 1.68 + 5.37, 0.49 + 12.82, 158.3 + 247.46, 601.92 + 37.74, and so on.

- They should then use the digits 1 to 9 once each to complete different additions in the form as shown. They try to find the addition with the largest and smallest sum.

Plenary

- Invite the children to explain an example of their own choosing from the work above.

- Ask them to talk through how they solved it and why they decided on a particular method.

- Ask for different approaches and any different answers.

Multiplication and Division (1)

Outcome

Children will be able to select appropriate informal or formal methods to solve multiplication calculations

Medium-term plan objectives

- Consolidate all previous work.

- Understand and use relationships between the four operations, and the principles of the arithmetic laws.

- Use related facts and doubling or halving, for example: halve an even number, double the other; to multiply by 25, multiply by 100, then divide by 4.

- Approximate first. Use informal pencil-and-paper methods to support, record or explain multiplications and divisions.

- Extend written methods to ThHTU multiplied by U, and short multiplication involving decimals.

Overview

- Using inverse operations to find the missing number.

- Informal written methods to support multiplication.

- Multiply four-digit and decimal numbers using written methods.

How you could plan this unit

	Stage 1	Stage 2	Stage 3	Stage 4	Stage 5
Content and vocabulary	Finding the missing number *double, halve, inverse, multiply, divide*	Gelosia or grid multiplication *array, row, column, digit, place, place-value, exchange*	Using informal methods to solve multiplications *jotting, method, strategy*	Multiplying ThHTU by U and U.th by U *tens, hundreds, thousands, units, tenths, hundredths*	
Notes	Resource page A				

48

Finding the missing number

Oral/mental starter
p 175

Advance Organiser

We are going to find the missing number

You will need: resource page A (one per child)

Whole-class work

- Draw this diagram on the board.

- *Who can tell me what the diagram means? What do we have to find out? How can we do that?*

- Discuss various strategies. Encourage the children to suggest using the inverse operation.

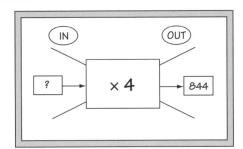

- *What times 4 makes 844? How could we rewrite that sentence?*

- Write on the board: $844 \div 4 = \square$.

- Now write this diagram on the board to illustrate the relationship.

- Work through the solution with the children, allowing them to suggest different methods. Encourage the children to suggest halving then halving again rather than written division.

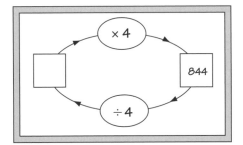

- Repeat for another example, such as $784 \div \square = 8$.

- Again, work through the example with the children, asking them to suggest the best method for solving the problem. Encourage them to point out that the relationship here is that $784 \div 8 = \square$. Work through the division with the class. Encourage them either to use short division or repeated halving.

Independent, paired or group work

- Ask the children to work in pairs. Each child solves the problems on resource page A, showing their working each time.

Plenary

- Ask the children to compare methods for solving the problems.

- *Who had a different way of finding the answer? Did anyone find anything different?*

- Make a list of different ways to solve each problem on the board, and check the answers with the class.

(**PUPIL PAGE**)

Name: _____

Find the missing numbers

$\boxed{} \times 9 = 171$ $891 \div \boxed{} = 33$

$4 \times \boxed{} = 564$ $\boxed{} \times 7 = 532$

$\boxed{} \div 6 = 534$ $5 \times \boxed{} = 480$

$423 \div \boxed{} = 9$ $82.6 \div \boxed{} = 8.26$

$\boxed{} \div 7.6 = 8$ $\boxed{} \div 9.2 = 64.4$

Gelosia or grid multiplication

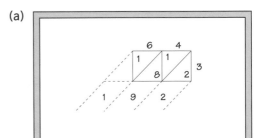

Advance Organiser

We are going to try another way of carrying out long multiplication

Oral/mental starter
p 175

Whole-class work

- Tell the children you are going to show them a new way to help them multiply.

- *Arab mathematicians first used this method over 800 years ago. It was introduced into Italy and has taken its name from the Italian word for grid (gelosia).*

- Draw diagram **(a)** on the board.

- *Who can tell me the answer? Where is the answer on the grid? How does the method work?*

- Encourage the children to explain in their own words how the gelosia method works.

- If necessary, prompt that the number at the top and the number at the side are the numbers we are multiplying. The digits of each number are multiplied together to make the numbers in the cells. The children then add the numbers in diagonal lines to find the answer.

- Ask the children to help you with a more complex example, such as 264 × 53.

(a)

(b)

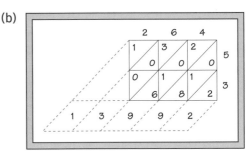

Independent, paired or group work

- Ask the children to use this or any other method to solve the following multiplications: 353 × 27, 456 × 38, 489 × 34, 567 × 78, 786 × 59.

- Encourage them to lay out their working carefully so they can explain it to another child.

Plenary

- Ask some pairs to demonstrate the jottings or diagrams they have used to show how the method works.

- Ask other children to think of different ways to solve the same problem.

- Discuss with them the fact that different methods can be useful for different calculations and that it is important to choose the best method each time.

Using informal methods to solve multiplications

Advance Organiser

We are going to look at rewriting multiplication calculations to make the process simpler

Oral/mental starter p 175

Whole-class work

- Write on the board: *45 × 24.*

- Ask the children to suggest methods of solving the problem. Ask them to identify the method they would find easiest for this calculation and why they think that.

- Ask the children to demonstrate various methods on the board. Ask the class to comment on how to do it. Confirm any methods the children use and go through them on the board.

- *Multiplying 45 by 24 by doubling 45 to 90 and halving 24 to 12.*

- *Multiplying 45 × 24 using a grid method.*

- *Which of these products would not be easy to find using the doubling and halving method? Why is that? 35 × 27, 25 × 34, 75 × 29, 65 × 36.*

- *Why is the doubling and halving method very useful when multiplying by a two-digit number ending in 5?*

- Write on the board: *25 × 26.*

- Ask the children for techniques to solve this problem. Include doubling and halving to 50 × 13 and using the fact that there are 4 lots of 25 in 100, multiplying by 100 and dividing by 4.

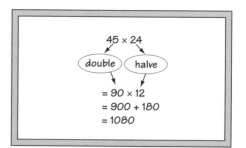

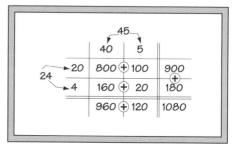

Independent, paired or group work

- Give the children calculations to discuss in pairs to decide on a suitable strategy. 25 × 44, 25 × 46, 65 × 32, 27 × 25, 62 × 65, 24 × 85, 34 × 25, 26 × 75, 77 × 25.

- Ask the children to calculate using their preferred strategy, and check a different method.

Plenary

- Ask for volunteers to select a calculation and discuss their chosen strategy.

- *Why did you choose that method? Who chose a different one? How could we check our answer? Which method do you find easiest? Why do you think that was?*

Multiplying ThHTU by U, and U.th by U

Advance Organiser

We are going to multiply large numbers and decimals by a single-digit number

Oral/mental starter
p 175

Whole-class work

- Write on the board: 7865 × 8.

- *Who can tell me a word sentence to go with this calculation?*

- Take a variety of suggestions and, if necessary, prompt with the following questions.

- *Who can use these phrases and words in a sentence that describes the sentence? Multiplied by, multiply, times, lots of.*

- *Can anyone suggest a story or a situation that fits this number statement?*

- *Who can suggest a good way of getting an approximation of the answer?*

- If the children suggest an approximation, ask them to think about whether the answer will be a bit less than the approximation or a bit more than the approximation.

- *Leah, you used the approximation 8000 × 8. Huw used 7900 × 10. Do you think the answer is a bit more or a bit less than your approximations? Why?*

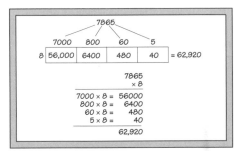

- Ask for methods to solve the problem and work through them on the board.

- Write on the board: 3.65 × 6.

- Ask the children how they would solve it. Suggest using the same method and ask the children to help you work through it on the board.

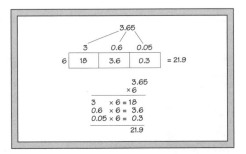

Independent, paired or group work

- Ask the children to follow the same process to work out these problems. They should be able to explain how they did each one.

  2448 × 5, 8505 × 7, 9540 × 9, 4.29 × 7, 8.55 × 8.

Plenary

- Work through an example together with the class, such as 7.27 × 8.

- Ask for volunteers to demonstrate different methods for solving the problem, and talk about how they are similar or different.

Multiplication and Division (2)

Outcome

Children will be able to select and use an appropriate written or mental method to solve division and multiplication questions

Medium-term plan objectives

- Consolidate all previous work.
- Use brackets.
- Use factors.
- Use closely related facts.
- Partition; for example $87 \times 6 = (80 \times 6) + (7 \times 6)$, $3.4 \times 3 = (3 \times 3) + (0.4 \times 3)$.
- Extend written methods to short division of TU or HTU by U (mixed number answer) and of decimals.

Overview

- Consolidate use of brackets.
- Extend written methods of division to HTU by TU.
- Consolidate selection of appropriate mental methods of multiplication.
- Extend written methods of division to TU.th by U.

How you could plan this unit

	Stage 1	Stage 2	Stage 3	Stage 4	Stage 5
	Using brackets	Short division of HTU by TU	Mental strategies for multiplication	Written division of TU.th by U	
Content and vocabulary	*split, separate, arrange, rearrange, describe, define, identify*	*share, divide, divided by, divided into, divisible by, remainder*	*factor*	*tenth, hundredth, digit, decimal, decimal point*	
Notes					

Using brackets

Oral/mental starter
p 175

Advance Organiser

We are going to learn how to use brackets to make calculation easier

Whole-class work

- Revisit partitioning to aid multiplication of a two-digit number by a single-digit number.

- Write on the board: *47 × 7.*

- *Who can show us how to solve this problem?*

- Take different ideas from the children and discuss each one. If no one mentions it, demonstrate partitioning on the board, talking through what happens at every stage and ensuring children understand the role of the brackets.

- Repeat for multiplying two two-digit numbers together.

- Again, ask the children to explain in their own words what is happening.

- Alternatively, or in addition, show this using a grid method.

- Write on the board: *3.4 × 6.*

- *Who can show us how to solve this problem? Who can show me how to do it?*

- Encourage the children to demonstrate using brackets and/or the grid method, as above.

$$47 \times 7$$
$$= (40 + 7) \times 7$$
$$= (40 \times 7) + (7 \times 7)$$
$$= 280 + 49$$
$$= 329$$

$$26 \times 37$$
$$= (20 + 6) \times (30 + 7)$$
$$= (20 \times 30) + (6 \times 30) + (20 \times 7) + (6 \times 7)$$
$$= 600 + 180 + 140 + 42$$
$$= 962$$

Independent, paired or group work

- Ask the children to rearrange and solve the following, showing the use of brackets. They can use the grid format, to assist them, if preferred.

  24 × 6, 4.5 × 6, 26 × 48, 35 × 27, 54 × 67, 34 × 29, 24 × 0.4, 56 × 0.2, 21 × 0.7, 37 × 0.3, 31 × 0.7, 34 × 0.3, 29 × 0.5, 14 × 0.9, 56 × 0.7.

Plenary

- Take feedback from the children about how they solved the problems.

- Discuss how the children could use brackets to solve multiplications of three-digit by two-digit numbers and of two decimals. Work through some of their ideas on the board.

Short division of HTU by TU

Oral/mental starter
p 175

Advance Organiser

We are going divide 896 by 28 using a written method

Whole-class work

- Write on the board: 896 ÷ 28.

- *Who can tell me how we can work this out? Who can make an approximation of the answer? How did you do that?*

- Encourage the children to think of a word problem that fits the number statement.

- Draw the following example on the board and ask the children to explain what is happening at each stage: *I know 28 × 20 makes 560 so there are at least 20 lots of 28 in 896. There was 336 left over so I subtracted another 10 lots of 28. I know 28 × 2 makes 56 so I took this away. I added up what I had done and it made 32 lots of 28. I checked by multiplying 28 by 32 using partitioning and it made 896.*

```
28)896
    560  = 20 × 28
   ²³̶³̶6
    280  = 10 × 28
     56  =  2 × 28
         = 32 × 28
```

- Ask for a volunteer to describe each stage of the calculation. Ask if anyone can solve the problem another way.

- Show the children the following alternative method and talk them through what happens.

```
        32
   28)896
     -84
      56
     -56
       0
```

Independent, paired or group work

- Ask the children to find the answers to the following calculations and to be able to explain their answer and how they reached it each time. Encourage them to approximate first.

874 ÷ 38	672 ÷ 48
744 ÷ 24	736 ÷ 16
592 ÷ 37	783 ÷ 27
456 ÷ 38	1134 ÷ 9
595 ÷ 35	

Plenary

- Work through some of the examples together asking different children to take up the commentary at the different steps of the calculation.

- Compare methods of working and ask the children to check their answers.

Mental strategies for multiplication

Advance Organiser

We are going to carry out multiplication calculations in our heads using two methods

Oral/mental starter p 175

Whole-class work

- Write on the board: 35×24.

- *What is the answer? Who can work it out in their head? How did you do that? How could you start?*

- Take a few ideas. Look for children to suggest, for example, using factors. Demonstrate on the board, asking the children to direct you.

- Ask the children to explain how they think the answer has been reached.

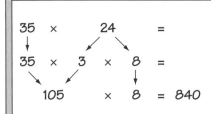

- Establish that 3 and 8 are factors of 24. Revise the word *factor* by asking for children to describe what it means: for example, the factors of a number are those numbers which divide exactly into that number.

- Discuss other mental strategies; for example, doubling and halving to 70×12 or doubling and halving repeatedly to reach 280×3.

- Extend to decimal numbers using other strategies; for example, multiplying 5.6×9 by partitioning into $(0.6 \times 9) + (5 \times 9)$ or using factors and multiplying $(5.6 \times 3) \times 3$.

Independent, paired or group work

- Tell the children that they have a chance to practise some of the strategies using pencil-and-paper jottings for 20 minutes before trying the strategies, mentally, in the plenary session.

- Ask them to think of mental strategies to solve: 34×15, 35×18, 45×16, 32×24, 76×8, 4.8×6, 83×7, 7.7×8, and so on.

Plenary

- Ask the children to work in groups of three, but each should have their own board to display the answer.

- For each group in turn, ask one child to suggest a strategy, another child to describe the first stage of the calculation and the third to give an answer. Change which children give which answer for different calculations. Ask the rest of the class if they agree each time.

Written division of TU.th by U

Advance Organiser

We are going to look at ways to divide decimal numbers by a single-digit number

**Oral/mental starter
p 175**

Whole-class work

- Write on the board: *79.2 ÷ 11.*

- *Who can tell me how to solve this problem? How should we begin?*

- Encourage the children to make an estimate; for example, in this case estimating *80 divided by 10.* Ask for volunteers to suggest methods of working through the problem. Ask them to suggest a context for the problem; for example, money. Take a variety of suggestions and, if necessary, prompt with these questions.

- *Who can use these phrases and words in a sentence that describes the calculation? Divided by, divided into, share.*

- Work through, using a written method of division on the board, to find the answer.

- Ask the children to explain what is happening at each stage. Include alternative methods as they are suggested, or suggest them as necessary.

$$11 \overline{)79.2}$$
$$-\underline{77} = 7 \times 11$$
$$2.2 = 0.2 \times 11$$
$$= 7.2 \times 11$$

I know $\frac{1}{10}$ of 11 is 1.1
So 2.2 must be $\frac{2}{10}$ of 11

Independent, paired or group work

- Ask the children to complete the following divisions using whatever method they prefer. Tell them they will need to lay out their working carefully so they can check their work and explain what they did to someone else. Encourage them to approximate first.

$47.9 \div 6$	$99.3 \div 6$
$36.8 \div 9$	$34.8 \div 5$
$45.7 \div 7$	$87.4 \div 8$

Plenary

- Take some examples and ask the children to work through how they solved them. Ask for different methods and answers.

- Compare how the different stages of the methods work, asking the children to spot when an equivalent calculation is being performed and when an alternative one is used.

Multiplication and Division (3)

Outcome

Children will be able to use complex written methods to solve problems, and express their answers in the appropriate form

Medium-term plan objectives

- Consolidate all previous work.
- Express a quotient as a fraction, or as a decimal rounded to one decimal place.
- Divide pounds and pence by a two-digit number to give pounds and pence.
- Round up or down after division, depending on the context.
- Use known facts and place-value to multiply and divide mentally.
- Use relationship between multiplication and division.
- Multiply HTU by TU.
- Divide HTU by TU (long division, whole number answer).

Overview

- Quotients as fractions and decimals.
- Division, in the context of money.
- Express the result of a division in context.
- Check, using multiplication and division.
- Long multiplication in extended and compact form.

How you could plan this unit

	Stage 1	Stage 2	Stage 3	Stage 4	Stage 5	Stage 6
Content and vocabulary	Expressing quotients as fractions or rounded decimals	Dividing amounts of money	Rounding after division, in context	Using the relationship between multiplication and division	Long multiplication of ThHTU by U	Concise written method of short multiplication
	quotient, fraction, decimal, factor, remainder	*money, pound, pence, penny, £*	*explain your reasoning/answer, describe, decide, choose*	*inverse*		*adjust*
Notes						

59

Expressing quotients as fractions or rounded decimals

Oral/mental starter p 175

Advance Organiser

We are going to write answers to divisions in different ways

Whole-class work

- Write on the board: $576 \div 5 = \square$.

- *Who can help me work this out? Who wants to make an approximation of the answer? Will the answer be a whole number, or not? How do you know?*

- Encourage the children to spot that 576 is not a multiple of 5 and that therefore the answer will not be a whole number.

- Work through the calculation on the board, asking the children to give you different ways of working out each stage.

- When you reach an answer with a remainder, ask the children how else you could write the answer. Encourage them to suggest a fraction or decimal of 1.

- *How can we work that out?*

- Point out that we can express the answer as a fraction by dividing the remainder by the divisor.

- *We divided 576 by 5. Our answer was 115 remainder 1. To express this as a fraction or decimal we divide the remainder, 1, by the divisor, 5.*

- Ask the children to give the answer $\frac{1}{5}$ or 0.2.

- *I divided 425 by 3 and my answer is 141 remainder 2. What is that as a fraction? What about as a decimal? What is 0.66666 rounded to one decimal place?*

$$576 \div 5 = 115 \text{ remainder } 1$$
$$1 \div 5 = \frac{1}{5} \text{ or } 0.2$$
$$576 \div 5 = 115\frac{1}{5} \text{ or } 125.2$$

Independent, paired or group work

- Ask the children to find answers to the following divisions, expressing their answer as a fraction and as a decimal: $390 \div 8$; $345 \div 10$; $325 \div 4$; $288 \div 5$; $250 \div 7$; $210 \div 8$; $169 \div 9$; $150 \div 12$.

Plenary

- Ask the children to read out some answers and how they reached them.

- Establish that sometimes the context might suggest one form rather than another.

- *How would I give the answer to dividing £2 among five people? How about dividing six apples among 12 people?*

Dividing amounts of money

Oral/mental starter
p 175

Advance Organiser

We are going to look at ways to divide amounts of money

Whole-class work

- Read the following problem to the children and ask them to listen carefully. Ask them to visualise what is happening at each stage.

- *Paramount pens cost £15.84 for a pack of 12. How much does each individual pen in the pack cost?*

- Ask for ideas on how to solve it. Ask the children to demonstrate or describe, or otherwise model, various methods.

- Ask the children at each stage to describe what is happening and to suggest other ways of finding the answer.

$$
\begin{array}{r}
12 \overline{)\ 15.84} \\
-\ 12.00\ =\quad £1 \times 12 \\
\hline
3.84 \\
-\ 3.60\ =\quad 30p \times 12 \\
\hline
0.24\ =\quad 2p \times 12 \\
\hline
£1.32 \times 12
\end{array}
$$

- Try a different context: *Two people share a bill of £21.21. They want to pay equal amounts. How much does each pay?*

- Again, work through various explanations with the children. At some point the question of how to divide 1p between two people will come up. Encourage the children to see that in this context there will be 1p left over that they cannot divide.

Independent, paired or group work

- Give the children the following problems and ask them to write an answer to each, in context.

- *A group of 15 friends have won £875 in a lottery. What would each person receive if the money were shared out equally?*

- *If a crate of 12 bottles of cola costs £4.75, how much should each bottle cost?*

- *Fourteen friends want to share the cost of a meal between them. The bill is £125.50. How much should each person pay?*

Plenary

- Ask some children to demonstrate the method they used to solve the problems.

- Discuss how the answers were reached, in context.

- Ask for different opinions and methods, and check the answers.

Rounding after division, in context

Oral/mental starter p 175

Advance Organiser

We are going to answer divisions in real-life contexts, giving sensible answers

Whole-class work

- Write the following problem on the board and read it out to the children. Ask them to listen carefully and picture what is happening.

> A school has been raising funds to buy new computers. A complete system will cost £840. There is currently £6500 in the fund. How many computer systems will they be able to buy?

- Work through the stages of problem-solving.

- *What do we know? What do we need to know? How can we find that out?*

- Encourage the children to approximate first and to explain what they have to do in their own words.

- Work through the suggested methods for calculating the answer. The answer is 7 with a remainder of £620.

- *How should we express this answer? What would be the solution in the real world?*

- Discuss possible answers of 8, 7, 7.7, $7\frac{3}{4}$. Encourage the children to look at the context and confirm that the solution in the real world would involve a remainder answer: they buy seven computer systems and have £620 left over.

- Repeat for another problem, such as *I have 6 litres of juice. How many glasses with a capacity of 240 ml can I fill?*

Independent, paired or group work

- Ask the children to answer the following problems, giving the appropriate answer, and their reason for choosing to answer in that form.

- Ask the children to set out their working so they can explain what they did.

- *The library needs new shelves for a new delivery of 945 books. Each shelf unit can hold a maximum of 85 books. How many shelf units must they order?*

- *The club's CD fund contains £54.85 and CDs from the regular supplier cost £8.45. How many can they buy?*

- *Golf balls are packed in boxes containing 84 balls. If 950 are produced in one hour, how many boxes are needed in each hour?*

Plenary

- If any children have created their own problems, give them the opportunity to read them out and take the class through the process described above.

Using the relationship between multiplication and division

Advance Organiser

We are going to check multiplication and division calculations

Oral/mental starter p 175

Whole-class work

- Practise some 'missing number' operations with the children.

- *I start with 37 and add 48. My new total is 85. What operation should I use to get back to 37 in one move?*

- *I multiply 15 by 9 to 135. How do I get back to 15 in one move?*

- Remind the children, if necessary, of the technique of using the inverse operation.

- Read out the following word problem and ask them to picture their heads in what is happening and decide what they need to do to solve it.

- *The perimeter of a regular octagon is 28.8 m. What is the length of each side?*

- Ask for ideas on how to solve the problem.

- *What do we know about a regular octagon? What do we know about perimeter? What operation do we need to know to find the length of each side?*

- Encourage the children to suggest that the perimeter of a regular octagon is equal to 8 times the length of one side. So to find the length of one side you need to divide 28.8 by 8.

- Work through the solution with the children.

Independent, paired or group work

- Tell the children that you have some real-life problems and you want them to check the answers. If the answer is wrong, you want them to write what it should be.

- *£1320 prize money was shared between 24 people. Each received £55.*

- *125 tickets costing £3.50 for the school concert were sold. The total was £187.50.*

- *The school buys 27 calculators for a total of £364.50. This means each one cost £13.50.*

- *The cinema sold 198 tickets to* Babe 4: Pig in Space. *The tickets were £4.25 each, so the cinema took £845.50 in total.*

- *The safari park took £1320 in total. The tickets are all £4.80, so 285 people must have bought tickets.*

Plenary

- Ask the children to describe how they checked the problems and what answers they found instead.

- Discuss any differences of opinion and check using another method to make sure.

Long multiplication of ThHTU by U

Oral/mental starter
p 175

Advance Organiser

We are going to practise multiplication with a written method

Whole-class work

- Write on the board: 2863 × 7.

- *Who can tell us how to solve this problem? Who can explain what we have to do in their own words? Can anyone suggest a story or a situation that fits this number sentence? Who can suggest a good way of getting an approximate answer?*

- Rounding a four-digit number to the nearest 1000 and a one-digit number to the nearest 10 is a good strategy but there may be others.

- *If we make an approximate answer by multiplying 3000 by 10, would we expect the real answer to be more than or less than our approximation?*

- Work through finding the solution using the two methods shown below. Encourage the children to describe what happens at each stage.

$$
\begin{array}{r}
2863 \\
\times\, 7 \\
\end{array}
$$

$$
\begin{aligned}
3 \times 7 &= 21 \\
60 \times 7 &= 420 \\
800 \times 7 &= 5600 \\
2000 \times 7 &= 14000 \\
\hline
2863 \times 7 &= 20041
\end{aligned}
$$

2863			
2000	800	60	3

7	14000	5600	420	21	= 20041

Independent, paired or group work

- Ask the children to use one of these methods, or another method, to solve 3584 × 7, 3859 × 3, 8587 × 6.

- Early finishers can make up other multiplications and test each other.

Plenary

- Work through some of the examples together, asking different children to take up the commentary at the distinct steps of the calculation.

Concise written method of short multiplication

Advance Organiser

We are going to use a quick way of solving written multiplication calculations

**Oral/mental starter
p 175**

Whole-class work

- Write on the board: 3584 × 7.

- Ask the children how you could solve it using written multiplication. (Refer back to the previous page for a visual description of how to solve this problem.)

- *Who can describe what is happening? Who can describe how I found this answer?*

- Tell the children that there is an even quicker way of recording this type of calculation.

- *We can combine our mental maths with our written maths to make multiplication easier and quicker.*

- Build up the following multiplication on the board, as shown.

- *First we multiply 4 × 7 to make 28. We write the units digit here and write the tens digit under the next column. Who can tell me why we do that?*

- *Then we multiply the next digit. Who can tell me what that is? What does 80 × 7 make? Who knows what we do next?*

- Demonstrate adding the 'carried' 2 to make 58. Write the 8 digit and 'carry' the 5.

- *Now who thinks they know what happens next? Who can describe the next stage?*

- Build up the multiplication until it is complete.

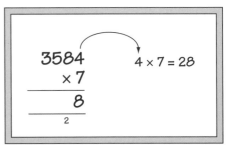

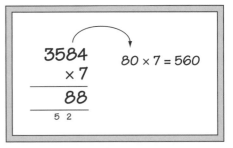

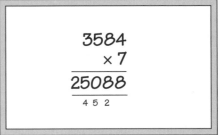

Independent, paired or group work

- Ask the children to use this method, or another if they find it more appropriate, to solve 4825 × 6, 5678 × 5, 7894 × 8, 6398 × 7.

Plenary

- Work through some examples together, asking different children to take up the commentary at the distinct steps of the calculation.

Solving Problems (1)

Outcome

Children will be able to use estimation to solve problems and check answers

Medium-term plan objectives	• Use all four operations to solve money or 'real life' word problems.
	• Choose appropriate operations/calculation methods.
	• Explain working.
	• Check by estimating.
	• Use inverse operation including with a calculator.

Overview	• Approximate answers to problems.
	• Use estimation to solve problems.
	• Use inverse operations to check answers.

How you could plan this unit

	Stage 1	Stage 2	Stage 3	Stage 4	Stage 5
Content and vocabulary	Using estimates to start solving problems *estimate, estimation, roughly, nearly, about, give or take, rounded to the nearest, approximate, approximation, ≈, approximately*	Narrowing down potential answers			
Notes	Resource page A				

Using estimates to start solving problems

Advance Organiser

We are going to use an estimate to make solving a word problem easier

Oral/mental starter
pp 175–176

Whole-class work

- Write the following word problem on the board. Read it out and ask children to listen carefully as you do so. They should visualise it in their heads and try to imagine what is happening – are things being put together, split apart, shared out, built up?

- *This year 25,500 lemmings plummeted from cliffs. Last year the number of lemmings plummeting was 4658 more. How many plummeted last year?*

- Encourage the children to make an estimate first. In this case they can round 4658 to 4500, or to 5000, and quickly arrive at an approximate answer.

- *Vicki, you thought about 30,000 lemmings plummeted last year. How can you use that approximation to find an answer?*

- Establish that a quick way is to work out that 4658 is 158 more than 4500, so the actual answer will be 30,158. Similarly, an approximation of 30,500 is 342 more than the answer as 5000 is 342 more than 4658.

- Repeat for another problem: *Jack plants his magic beans in rows. He plants 28 rows of 45 beans. How many beans did he plant altogether?*

- Again, encourage the children to visualise the problem in order to identify the necessary operation. Suggest that they make an approximation of the answer in order to start to solve the problem.

- *Tammy, you made an approximation of 30 × 45. How can you use that to begin to solve the problem?*

- Establish that if 30 × 45 makes 1350, then 28 × 45 will make 1350 minus 2 lots of 45.

Independent, paired or group work

- Ask the children to complete the problems on resource page A.

- Encourage them to estimate their answer first and to use that answer as a starting point for solving the problem.

Plenary

- Invite some of the children to explain how they solved some of the problems.

- Discuss different methods they used for each problem.

- Work through checking the answers using the inverse operation.

Name: _____

Making estimates

1   Balbo Biggins walks 28 km every day. If he walks for 19 days, how far does he walk in total?

2   Maisie steals 43 pieces of cheese every month. If she steals cheese for 16 months, how much cheese is that in total?

3   At the butterfly ball there are 3580 guests. If one table seats 8 guests, how many tables will they need to seat all the guests?

4   The average monkey eats 758 bananas a year. Simon the monkey eats 1467 bananas a year. How many more bananas does Simon eat than the average monkey?

5   Every minute 243 cars pass a speed camera. How many pass it in one hour?

6   A school has 146 pupils. This year 29 pupils leave but 74 pupils join. The school will need a new classroom if they have more than 200 pupils. Will they need a new classroom?

7   A branch of McBurger's sells 486 meals each day. How many do they sell in 17 days?

Classworks © Classworks Numeracy author team, Nelson Thornes Ltd, 2003

Narrowing down potential answers

Advance Organiser

We are going to solve a question by using what we know

Oral/mental starter pp 175–176

Whole-class work

- Write the following word problem on the board and ask children to listen carefully while you read it out.

- *Square baking trays have rows and columns of spaces for pies. Each tray has the same number of rows as columns. If you stack the same number of trays together as each tray has columns and the stack can hold 27 pies altogether, how many trays are in the stack?*

- Ask the children to imagine what is happening. Ask for volunteers to describe, in their own words, what is being asked. Encourage the children to visualise a group of arrays and to suggest multiplication.

- Draw the following diagram on the board and ask the children how it relates to the problem.

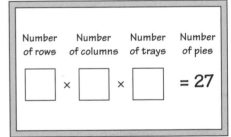

- Encourage them to realise that each box is part of the stack – and that the problem is solved by finding the missing numbers that multiply to make 27.

- Work through trial-and-improvement on the board. Suggest that the children start with, say, $2 \times 2 \times 2$ and $4 \times 4 \times 4$ to reach the answer, or to begin with $3 \times 9 = 27$.

- *What if every stack held 125 pies? How many trays then?*

- Rub out 27 and write 125. Ask the children to discuss how to solve this problem.

- Show them, if necessary, how to use approximation, and trial-and-improvement, to get close.

- Suggest, for example, trying $4 \times 4 \times 4$, and $10 \times 10 \times 10$, then narrowing down the answer.

- Ask them to use a calculator and trial-and-improvement to find the correct number (5).

Independent, paired or group work

- Ask the children to solve similar problems, involving 512, 1331, 3375, 6859, and so on.

Plenary

- Invite the children to explain how they solved some of the problems.

- Ask them to suggest alternative methods and answers.

- Ask for ideas for how to check each answer.

Solving Problems (2)

Outcome

Children will be able to use visual models in problem-solving activities

Medium-term plan objectives

- Use all four operations to solve money or 'real life' word problems.
- Choose appropriate operations/calculation methods.
- Explain working.

Overview

- Visualise problems.
- Solve problems with visual support and jottings.
- Use □ and △ to express and solve word problems.

How you could plan this unit

	Stage 1	Stage 2	Stage 3	Stage 4	Stage 5
Content and vocabulary	Visual approaches to problem solving *fraction, mixed number, proper fraction, improper fraction, vulgar fraction, numerator, denominator, common denominator, equivalent fraction*	Alternative visual methods for solving problems *missing number, symbol, strategy*			
Notes	Resource page A	Resource page B			

Visual approaches to problem solving

Advance Organiser

We are going to solve problems by visualising what happens

Oral/mental starter pp 175–176

You will need: resource page A (one per child)

Whole-class work

- Read a quick word problem to the children: *Three-fifths of a number is 27. What is the whole number?*

- Ask the children to discuss how to solve the problem. Ask them to visualise what is happening. Invite the children to explain the problem in their own words or to share their visualisations.

- Draw the following diagram on the board and ask the children what they think it means, in the context of the problem.

- Discuss how to proceed. Lead the children towards finding *one-fifth* of the number by dividing 27 (*three-fifths*) by 3. Write 9 in each of the fifth squares on the board.

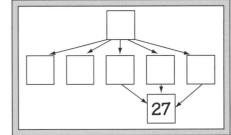

- Complete the problem, showing as a check that as $\frac{1}{5}$ of 45 = 9, $\frac{2}{5}$ of 45 = 9 + 9 and $\frac{3}{5}$ of 45 = 9 + 9 + 9, which makes 27.

- *Andrea used $\frac{2}{3}$ of her money to buy a book. The book cost £3.20. How much money did she have to begin with?*

- Again, ask the children to visualise what is happening. Illustrate a visual approach on the board.

- *If £3.20 is $\frac{2}{3}$ of the whole amount then $\frac{1}{3}$ of the whole amount must be half of £3.20. The total amount must be $3 \times £1.60 = £4.80$.*

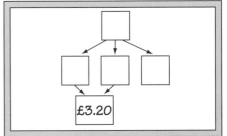

Independent, paired or group work

- Ask the children to complete resource page A.

Plenary

- Invite some of the children to explain how they solved some of the problems.

- Ask the children for alternative methods and steps and how you could check the answers.

- Some children may prefer more conventional methods to visual ones.

Name: _____

Solving problems

Find the answers to the following problems. You must show your working.

1 A set of marbles is shared equally between 5 children. There are 3 children who have a total of 54 marbles. How many marbles does each child have?
Show your working.

2 A car stops after 260 km. It still has $\frac{2}{5}$ of the journey to complete. How many more kilometres does it have to travel?
Show your working.

3 A ball of string had $\frac{4}{6}$ of its total length cut to leave 540 cm. What was the total length of the ball of string?
Show your working.

4 Two bags of flour have a total mass of 2.7 kg. One bag makes up $\frac{3}{5}$ of the total mass. What is the mass of each bag?
Show your working.

5 Donna bought a book for £6.99. She still had $\frac{2}{5}$ of her money left. How much money did she begin with?
Show your working.

Classworks © Classworks Numeracy author team, Nelson Thornes Ltd, 2003

Alternative visual methods for solving problems

Advance Organiser

We are going to solve problems involving missing numbers

Oral/mental starter pp 175–176

You will need: resource page B (one per child)

Whole-class work

- Write the following problem on the board. Ask the children to listen as you read it out and to visualise what happens at each stage.

- *An ice cream and a milkshake cost £5.00 altogether. An ice cream costs 70p less than a shake. How much did each item cost?*

- *How could you solve this problem?*

- Ask the children to suggest different ideas for solving the problem. Write some of them on the board.

- Draw the following diagram on the board and ask the children to tell you how it relates to the word problem.

- *The triangle is the cost of the ice cream. The milkshake costs 70p more than the ice cream, so we write 'triangle + 70p' for the cost of a milkshake. The total amount of £5.00 is represented by two triangles plus 70p.*

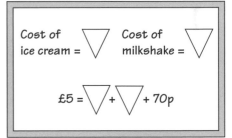

- Go through each part of the calculation above. Encourage the children to express what is happening in different ways.

- *We subtract 70p from £5.00. What does that make? What do we do next? How did you decide that?*

- Work through finding £4.30 as being equal to two triangles and dividing that by 2 to make £2.15.

- *One triangle is worth £2.15. So what costs £2.15? How much does a milkshake cost? How can we check?*

Independent, paired or group work

- Ask the children to solve some of the problems on resource page B using whatever method they find most useful. Suggest visual aids where appropriate.

Plenary

- Invite the children to explain how they solved some of the problems.

- Brainstorm solving problems involving three numbers, such as: *I spend 56p on one chew, some gum and a chocolate bar. The chew costs 15p less than the gum. The chocolate costs 20p more than the gum.*

Gum	$= \bigcirc$
Chew	$= \bigcirc - 15p$
Chocolate	$= \bigcirc + 20p$
56p	$= \bigcirc + \bigcirc + \bigcirc + 20p - 15p$

(PUPIL PAGE)

Name: _____

Solving problems with missing numbers

Find the answers to the following problems.

1 A CD and a tape cost £13.89. The CD cost £4.50 more than the tape.
How much did each item cost?

2 A book and a hat cost £19.40. The hat cost £1.77 more than the book.
How much did each item cost?

3 A shirt and a tie cost £35.99. The shirt cost £24.50 more than the tie.
How much did each item cost?

4 A pizza and a drink cost £11.55. The pizza cost £5.63 more than the drink.
How much did each item cost?

Solving Problems (3)

Outcome

Children will be able to demonstrate using decision-making to solve problems

Medium-term plan objectives

- Use all four operations to solve money or 'real life' word problems.
- Choose appropriate operations/calculation methods.
- Explain working.
- Check by estimating.
- Use inverse operation, including with calculator.

Overview

- Make decisions to interpret the answer to a problem.
- Explain decisions and working.
- Choose appropriate calculation methods.
- Explain solutions.

How you could plan this unit

	Stage 1	Stage 2	Stage 3	Stage 4	Stage 5
Content and vocabulary	Deciding on an answer, in context *calculate, calculation, operation, answer, reasonable, correct, accurate, exact, wrong, problem, solve, solution, method, inverse, roughly, approximately, round up, round down*	Deciding how to solve a problem *strategy, how did you work it out?, what could we try next?, tell me, describe, explain your method/answer/ reasoning*			
Notes		Resource page A			

Deciding on an answer, in context

Advance Organiser

We are going to find an answer and decide how to express it in context

Oral/mental starter pp 175–176

You will need: calculators

Whole-class work

- Read out a word problem and ask the children to visualise what is happening.

- *A 50 cm length of ribbon is cut into four equal pieces. How long is each piece?*

- When they have come up with a method and found an answer, write their answer on the board.

- *Darren, you halved and halved again and got the answer $12\frac{1}{2}$ cm. Becky knew that 4×12 made 48 and had the answer 12 cm with 2 cm of ribbon left over. In which form should we write our answer to the problem in this context?*

- Discuss how several different answers can make sense in this context. Repeat for a different problem.

- *Six people shared £50.00. How much money did they each receive?*

- Work out the answer using a calculator and with a mental or written method and discuss what form the answer can be in.

- *Does £8.333333 make sense in this context? Is £8 remainder £2 a sensible answer? What might happen to the remaining £2 in real life?*

- Repeat with 50 cm of wood cut into three equal lengths.

Independent, paired or group work

- Ask the children to work on some similar problems.

- *If 15 people share £5299 equally, how much do they each receive?*

- *A 15 metre piece of rope is cut into seven equal lengths. How long is each piece?*

- *If 260 children were divided into teams of six, how many teams could there be?*

- *The maximum number of ice creams that can be bought with a £10 note is 19. What is the cost of one ice cream?*

- *Seven children share turns on a computer game. They play for a total of 2 hours. How much time does each child get?*

Plenary

- Invite the children to explain how they solved some of the problems.

- *What calculation did you use? What was the answer? Do you need to round the answer up or down? Why?*

Deciding how to solve a problem

Advance Organiser

We are going to decide how best to solve some different problems

Oral/mental starter pp 175–176

You will need: calculators, resource page A (one per child)

Whole-class work

- Read a word problem to the children and ask them to listen carefully.

- *Orange Class are travelling to the theatre by minibus. Each minibus seats nine children. How many minibuses are needed if there are 30 children altogether in Orange Class?*

- Ask them to think about the problem and to visualise what is happening. Work through the problem and discuss how to round the answer sensibly.

- *Each minibus costs £29.00 to hire. Admission to the theatre costs £1.99 per child. What is the total cost of the trip? How much should each child be asked to pay?*

- Discuss the problem and ask the children to decide on how they will solve it. Encourage them to separate the problem into stages and to decide on an order for the solution.

- Ask the children to suggest different solutions and work through them all, asking the children to take up the description at different stages. Ensure they can identify an appropriate method for each stage – mental, written or calculator.

- They should work out that they need four minibuses and multiply £29.00 by 4 to make £116. Next they need to multiply £1.99 × 30 to make £59.70. Then they add the two amounts, to make £175.70, divide by 30 and round the answer appropriately.

- Discuss the real-life consequences of how they decide to round or adjust the answer.

- *Should the school charge too much or too little? Should some children be charged more than others?*

Independent, paired or group work

- Ask the children to complete resource page A.

Plenary

- Invite the children to explain how they solved some of the problems.

- Explain the importance of reading the question carefully.

- *How did you find the number of tables? Did you decide on the number of tables for each classroom, then add them, or add the children and find how many tables for all of them? Why would that make a difference?*

Name: _____

Deciding how best to solve problems

Read the questions carefully. Decide how to answer each one and look at each stage separately. You can use a calculator, if necessary.

> Green Class has 21 children
>
> Blue Class has 27 children
>
> Red Class has 30 children

1 Each classroom table can seat 5 children. How many tables are needed altogether?

2 A box of 12 pens costs £2.64 and a box of 24 pencils costs £2.90. How much does it cost to give every child in the three classes 1 pen and 2 pencils?

3 The school is given £600 to buy books for the children in these three classes. Explain what you think is the fairest way to share the money.

4 The three classes are going on a trip to a museum. There must be 1 adult to accompany each group of 10 children. How many adults are needed for the trip?

5 The children and adults travel by bus. Each bus can carry 17 people.

(a) How many buses are needed?

(b) How many children and adults travel on each bus?

6 Each child has paid £2.50 for the trip. Approximately 75% of this money is spent on bus fares and 25% on admission to the museum. How much does admission to the museum cost?

Classworks © Classworks Numeracy author team, Nelson Thornes Ltd, 2003

Solving Problems (4)

Outcome

Children will be able to use a variety of approaches to solve problems involving money and measurement

Medium-term plan objectives

- Use all four operations to solve word problems involving money or 'real life' measurement.
- Choose appropriate operations/calculation methods.
- Explain working.
- Check by adding in reverse order, including with a calculator.

Overview

- Solve problems involving measures.
- Solve problems involving time.
- Explain working.

How you could plan this unit

	Stage 1	Stage 2	Stage 3	Stage 4	Stage 5
Content and vocabulary	Problems involving measures *inverse, area, square centimetres, cm², capacity, full, litre, millilitre, length, width, height, perimeter, centimetre, metre, kilometre, foot, feet, inch, mass, weigh, kilogram, gram, pound, convert, mean, average*	Problems involving time *time, date, calendar, rate, speed, average speed, miles per hour (mph) kilometres per hour (km/h)*			
Notes	Resource page A	Resource page B			

Problems involving measures

Oral/mental starter pp 175–176

Advance Organiser

We are going to work out the capacity of two bottles

You will need: calculators, resource page A (one per child)

Whole-class work

- Write the following on the board and ask children to contribute to a list of facts about each of the units of measurement in the table; for example, 1 km = 1000 m.

1 metre	1 litre
1 foot	1 kilogram
1 kilometre	1 pound

- Practise adding some measures together; for example, 3.3 km, 0.9 km and 650 m.

- *What should we do first? How did you decide that?*

- Encourage them to simplify the problem by converting to common units.
  3300 m has the same value as   3.3 km
  900 m   has the same value as   0.9 km
  650 m   has the same value as   0.65 km

- Complete the problem and repeat for a word problem.

- *Two bottles hold a total of 2.62 litres. The larger bottle holds 220 ml more than the smaller bottle. What is the capacity of each bottle?*

- Encourage the children to suggest ways of solving the problem. Encourage a visual approach, moving towards recording the problem using □ and △. Convert to common units. Talk through the stages of the problem, as shown.

$$\square + \triangle = 2620 \text{ millilitres}$$
$$\triangle = \square + 220 \text{ millilitres}$$
$$\square + \square + 220 \text{ millilitres} = 2620 \text{ millilitres}$$
$$2620 \text{ ml} - 220 \text{ ml} = 2 \times \square$$
$$2400 \text{ ml} = 2 \times \text{ capacity of smaller bottle}$$
$$1200 \text{ ml} = \text{ capacity of smaller bottle}$$
$$1420 \text{ ml} = \text{ capacity of larger bottle}$$

Independent, paired or group work

- Ask the children to complete the problems on resource page A.

Plenary

- Invite the children to explain how they solved some of the problems.

- Ask them to suggest ways in which a calculator could be used to check their answers.

Name: _____

Solving problems involving measurement

Choose some of these problems to solve and write them in your book. Solve the problems and show your working. (You may get a mark in an exam.)

1   A rectangle has a perimeter of 10.5 m. The length measures twice the width. Write the length and width.

2   A bucket holds 6 litres of water. It takes 15 jugs or 24 cups full of water to fill the bucket. Write the capacity of the jug and the cup.

3   In a race, Sasha ran 2.6 km, cycled for 39,000 metres and swam 1.2 km. How far did she race in total?

4   The mass of 3 crates is 1.65 tonnes, 658 kg and 3.09 tonnes. What is their total mass?

5   $1\frac{3}{4}$ metres were cut from a length of rope measuring 13 metres. The remaining piece of rope was cut into 3 equal lengths. How long was each of these 3 equal lengths?

6   A sack of potatoes weighing 14.5 kg was divided into 3 bags. One of the bags weighed 100 g more than the other bags. How much did each bag weigh?

7   John is 6 feet 5 inches tall. There are 2.54 cm to 1 inch. What is John's height in centimetres? What else do I need to know?

8   Doris paid £3.00 for 16 lb of potatoes. Boris paid £3.00 for 16 kg of potatoes. Who got the greatest mass of potatoes for their money? What else do I need to know?

9   Ryan is 11 cm taller than Roulla. Dawn is 2 cm shorter than Roulla. The mean average height of the 3 children is 135 cm. What is the height of each child?

Classworks © Classworks Numeracy author team, Nelson Thornes Ltd, 2003

Problems involving time

Oral/mental starter
pp 175–176

Advance Organiser

We are going to solve problems involving different units of time

You will need: calculators, resource page B (one per child)

Whole-class work

- Write the following list on the board and ask the children to suggest facts about each unit; for example, there are 24 hours in a day, there are 12 months in a year, and so on.

Year	Day
Month	Hour
Week	Minute

- Read the following problem to the children. Ask them to listen carefully and visualise what is happening.

- *Dawn saved 20p per day. How much had she saved in seven weeks?*

- Encourage the children to discuss how to begin.

- *What do we need to find out? What do we know already?*

- Discuss finding how much she saves per week by multiplying 20p × 7 to make £1.40, then multiplying that by seven weeks to find the total, £9.80.

- Repeat for another problem, such as the following:

- *Find the number of whole days in 200,000 seconds.*

- Work through calculating how many seconds in a day (24 × 60 × 60) using a calculator.

- Ask the children to suggest the next step. Calculate 200,000 ÷ 86,400 and interpret the answer (2.31) appropriately as *two whole days*.

- Try some time problems that can be modelled on a time number line.

- *A loaf of bread was put into the oven 70 minutes before 7 am. What time was it put in?*

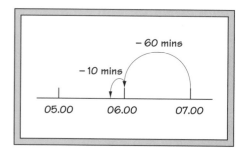

Independent, paired or group work

- Ask the children to complete resource page B.

Plenary

- Invite the children to explain how they solved some of the problems.

- Encourage them to show any visual aids such as number lines on the board.

- Discuss how to calculate fractions of different units of time by converting them into smaller units; for example, calculating one-quarter of one day, using hours (24 ÷ 4 = 6 hours).

Name: _____

Solving problems involving time

Solve the following problems. Show your working each time.

1 Jon's bus leaves at 08.40. It takes 125 minutes to get to the airport. What time does it arrive at the airport?

2 The next day, the traffic is much worse and the bus takes 196 minutes. What time does it arrive at the airport?

3 Amy spends on average 35 minutes per day on the bus. How long does she spend on the bus in a week?

4 Every week 432 buses break down on the motorway. How many break down in 3 months?

5 A bus journey costs 85p. How much does Ali spend in a month if he takes 5 bus journeys every week?

6 A pie comes out of the oven at 09.45. If it was cooked for 115 minutes, what time did it go into the oven?

7 A play lasts for one hour and three-quarters. There is an interval of 20 minutes as well. If it starts at 18.02, what time does it finish?

8 The 12.05 departure from Manchester arrives in Birmingham at 15.37. How long does it take to get there if it leaves on time? The train was supposed to arrive at 13.15. How late is it?

9 Jane and Ilesh are doing a sponsored silence. Jane is silent for 9 hours. Ilesh is silent for 534 minutes. Who is silent the longest and by how long?

10 Rob says he has been silent for 3.5 days. How many hours is that?

Solving Problems (5)

Outcome

Children will be able to use a range of strategies to solve problems involving percentages

Medium-term plan objectives	
	• Use all four operations to solve word problems involving money or 'real life', including finding percentages and VAT.
	• Choose appropriate operations/calculation methods.
	• Explain working.
	• Check using products of odd/even numbers or doing the inverse calculation, including using a calculator.

Overview	
	• Find percentages in context.
	• Check answers.
	• Solve problems involving VAT.
	• Explain working.

How you could plan this unit

	Stage 1	Stage 2	Stage 3	Stage 4	Stage 5
Content and vocabulary	Solving problems involving percentages *percentage, per cent, %, method, strategy, jotting, answer, correct, wrong, what could we try next?, how did you work it out?*	Problems involving VAT *discount, VAT*			
Notes	Resource page A				

Solving problems involving percentages

Advance Organiser

We are going to work out the price less 25%

Oral/mental starter pp 175–176

You will need: calculators, resource page A (one per child)

Whole-class work

- Read the following word problem to the children and ask them to visualise what is happening. Encourage them to rephrase the problem in their own words.

- *A hardback book costs £16. At Christmas the bookshop offers 25% off the price. What is the new price?*

- Ask the children to discuss how to solve the problem.

- Write some ideas on the board and encourage the children to share how they visualise the problem. Include methods such as the following:

- *How else could we write 25% of £16?*

- Discuss the equivalent fractions and decimals. Write: *25% of £16 is the same value as 0.25 of £16 and is the same value as $\frac{1}{4}$ of £16.*

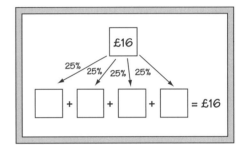

- Agree that a quick way to find 25% or $\frac{1}{4}$ of an amount is to divide by 4.

- *After Christmas the clothes shop has a January sale. Everything has 25% off. A pair of fabulous shoes costs £111 in the sale. How much did they cost originally?*

- Again, ask for ideas on how to solve the problem. Look for the children suggesting that £111 is 75% or $\frac{3}{4}$ of the original price. Encourage the children to work out that they could find $\frac{1}{4}$ of the original price by dividing £111 by 3. Provide a visual illustration of this if necessary.

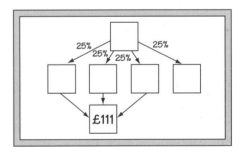

Independent, paired or group work

- Ask the children to complete resource page A.

Plenary

- Invite the children to explain, describe or illustrate how they solved some of the problems.

- *Did anyone do anything different? Who had a different answer?*

- *How did you check your answer?*

Name: _____

Solving problems involving percentages

Solve the following problems. Show your working each time.

1 Bella pays a deposit of 40% on a car. If the deposit is £1246, how much is the full price of the car?

2 A holiday is reduced in price by 10%. The reduced price is £702. What was the original price?

3 Jim says he spends 25% of his waking hours travelling. If he sleeps for 7 hours a night, how long does he spend travelling per day?

4 A water tank is 75% full. If it contains 2.325 litres, how much does it contain when it is full?

5 A flight is offered at a 30% discount. If the flight now costs £85.75, how much did it cost originally?

Classworks © Classworks Numeracy author team, Nelson Thornes Ltd, 2003

Problems involving VAT

Advance Organiser

We are going to solve problems by calculating amounts of value added tax (VAT)

Oral/mental starter
pp 175–176

You will need: calculators

Whole-class work

- Write on the board: *VAT = 17.5%*.

- Ask the children if they know what it means. Explain that VAT means 'value added tax' and is added to the prices of most things sold in shops. VAT is a government tax. Explain that the price you see in a shop or advert usually includes VAT, but not always.

- Ask the children to discuss how they could add 17.5% to a price.

- Encourage them to include a straightforward decimal method; for example, recognising that they need to find 117.5% of the price and multiply by 117.5.

- Also include a mental method, partitioning 17.5% into 10%, 5% and 2.5% using halving.

- *A suit costs £150 without VAT. What is the price with VAT added?*

- Discuss first finding 10% by dividing by 10.

- *How do you know that will work?*

- *10% of £150 is the same as $\frac{1}{10}$ of £150 and the same as £150 divided by 10. Who can work that out for us?*

- Continue by halving £15 to find 5%, halving again to find 2.5%, and adding the percentages. Add this to the £150 to find the new total.

- Demonstrate using the percentage button on a calculator – these differ, but a representative key-press order would be:

- *A sofa costs £200 including VAT. How much VAT is included in that price?*

- Discuss how this problem is different and what they need to do.

- Work through finding 1% and multiplying by 17.5 to find 17.5%. ´

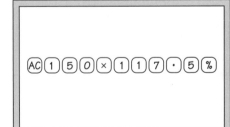

Independent, paired or group work

- Ask the children to copy down the following prices. They should write each one with VAT added. £100, £200, £250, £50, £80, £1000.

- Ask them to write their own amounts of money to swap with a partner. For these, they work out how much VAT is included in the price.

Plenary

- Invite the children to explain how they solved some of the problems.

- Work through some of the methods suggested by the children.

Solving Problems (6)

Outcome

Children will be able to use strategies and facts they already know to solve complex problems and to check their answers

Medium-term plan objectives	• Use all four operations to solve word problems involving money or 'real life', including percentages.
	• Choose appropriate operations/calculation methods.
	• Explain working.
	• Check using sums/differences of odd/even numbers or doing the inverse calculation, including using a calculator.
Overview	• Solve problems using knowledge of products of odd and even numbers.
	• Check answers including with a calculator.
	• Model multi-step problems visually.

How you could plan this unit

	Stage 1	Stage 2	Stage 3	Stage 4	Stage 5
Content and vocabulary	Multi-step problems involving money

inverse, product, multiply, divide, separate, split, adjust | Modelling and solving multi-step problems

investigate, decide, describe, define, explain your reasoning, draw, record, represent, show your working | | | |
| **Notes** | Resource page A | Resource page B | | | |

Multi-step problems involving money

Advance Organiser

We are going to solve problems in stages

You will need: calculators, resource page A (one per child and one enlarged)

Whole-class work

- Show the children an enlarged copy of resource page A.

- *Who can explain what the price list means? Who can describe what each part means? How much is a ticket in the north stand upper tier?*

- Try some more quick questions with the children.

- *How much would three tickets in the east stand lower tier cost?*

- Work through the separate stages with children, suggesting how to solve the problem at each stage.

- Read out a word problem to the children and ask them to listen carefully and visualise what is happening.

- *Gemma bought three tickets in the lower tier of one stand for £35.85. Which stand were the tickets in?*

- Encourage the children to separate the problem into stages and to use their knowledge of number facts to make an approximation of the answer, or to narrow down the range of potential answers.

- *We know Gemma bought three of the same sort of ticket and the tickets are for the lower tier. What else do we know?*

- Point out, for example, that the total has an odd number of pence, so the three tickets must each have an odd number of pence as well. Children may also approximate that south stand and north stand tickets will be too expensive as they are both about £15, and 3 × £15 makes £45.

- Try other examples: four tickets in the lower tier cost £59.20; seven tickets in the upper tier cost £166.25, and so on.

Independent, paired or group work

- Ask the children to solve the problems on resource page A. They should record how they did each one. They can use a calculator but must record what they did.

Plenary

- Invite the children to explain how they solved some of the problems.

- *Which of these amounts of money is odd £50, £5, 50p, 5p?*

- Ensure that the children know how to read the calculator display in regard to amounts of money.

- *Use the calculator to work out £14.80 × 3.*

- *What does 44.4 mean in this context?*

(**PUPIL PAGE**)

Name: _____

Ticket problems

Centenary Stadium

	Lower Tier	Upper Tier
North Stand	£15.99	£23.75
South Stand	£14.80	£24.90
East Stand	£11.95	£39.99
West Stand	£12.90	£40.90

1 Ian paid £60 for 3 tickets and got £15.60 change. Which sort of tickets did he buy?

2 Jade paid £60 for 4 tickets and got £8.40 change. Which sort of tickets did she buy?

3 Selma paid £80 for 3 tickets and got £8.75 change. Which sort of tickets did she buy?

4 David paid £100 for 4 tickets and got 40p change. Which sort of tickets did he buy?

5 Ahmed paid £279.93 for _____ tickets. Which sort of tickets did he buy?

6 I paid £204.50 for _____ tickets. Which sort of tickets did I buy?

Classworks © Classworks Numeracy author team, Nelson Thornes Ltd, 2003

Modelling and solving multi-step problems

Advance Organiser

We are going to solve complex problems and show how we did it

Oral/mental starter
pp 175–176

You will need: calculators, resource page B (one per child and one enlarged)

Whole-class work

- Show the children an enlarged copy of resource page B.

- *Who can tell me what this shows? What does each CD cost?*

- Read out a word problem and ask the children to listen carefully and visualise what is happening. Ask them to describe in their own words what the problem is asking them to find out and what they know already.

- *Lemar paid £38.97 for three copies of the same CD. Which CD did he buy?*

- Discuss strategies for solving the problem. Discuss how the children can make an approximation of what each CD should have cost and use this to start to solve the problem.

- *Scilla knows that £36 is equal to 3 × £12. She thinks that the CD must cost more than £12 each. Palash knows that 3 × £13 makes £39. He then worked out that the CD must cost £12.99 per copy as £38.97 is 3p less than £39.*

- Show them how to use a calculator to check the answer using an inverse operation; for example, multiplying 12.99 by 3 and interpreting the answer appropriately.

- *Could we have used the calculator to solve the problem?*

- Repeat for a more complex problem.

- *William paid for three CDs with three £20 notes. He was given £19.76 change. Which three CDs did he buy?*

- Demonstrate using a flow chart or diagram to model the problem visually.

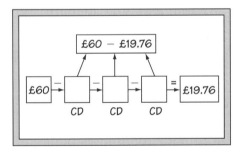

Independent, paired or group work

- Ask the children to complete the problems on resource page B. Support the children using flow charts to model the questions.

Plenary

- Invite the children to explain how they solved some of the problems.

- *How could you use your knowledge of odds and evens to help you solve this problem?*

- *How could you use inverse operations to solve this problem?*

- *How could you check your answer?*

(**PUPIL PAGE**)

Name: _____

Word problems

X-Club 4	*Greatest Hits*	£12.99
6Pac	*Even Greater Hits*	£14.50
Average Boy Band	*Really, Really Great Hits*	£15.93
TV Spin-Off	*The Best Hits ... Ever!*	£13.20
The Chimps	*The Only Hits Album You Need*	£12.54

1   Madge paid £52.80 for 4 copies of the same CD. Which CDs did she buy?

2   Gareth paid £79.65 for 5 copies of the same CD. Which CDs did he buy?

3   Will bought 3 copies of 1 CD and 1 copy of the Chimps CD for £60.33. Which CDs did he buy?

4   Britney bought 3 copies of 1 CD and 1 copy of the TV Spin-Off CD for £56.70.
       Which CDs did she buy?

5   Thom paid for 2 CDs with 2 £20 notes. He was given £14.47 change.
       Which 2 CDs did he buy?

6   Ayshah bought 3 copies of one CD and 3 copies of another. She paid £91.29.
       Which CDs did she buy?

7   Tjinder bought 16 copies of the same CD. He was given a 20% discount of £42.24.
       Which CDs did he buy?

8   Jennifer bought 13 copies of the same CD. She was given a 25% discount of £40.75.
       Which CDs did she buy?

9   Ozzy paid for 2 copies of the same CD with 2 £20 notes. He was given 1 note and 4 coins
       in his change.

       He could have bought 2 copies of _____

       or _____

       or _____

Measures (1)

Outcome

Children will be able to compare lengths of objects

Medium-term plan objectives	
	• Calculate perimeter of rectangles and simple compound shapes.
	• Use, read and write standard metric units of length, including abbreviations and relationships.
	• Convert larger to smaller units of length, and vice versa.
	• Know approximate metric equivalent for a mile.
	• Appreciate different times around the world.
	• Suggest suitable units and equipment to estimate or measure length.
	• Record estimates/measurements from scales to a suitable degree of accuracy.
	• Use all four operations to solve measurement word problems, including time.
	• Choose appropriate operations/calculation methods.
	• Explain working.

Overview	
	• Calculate perimeter including 'missing' dimensions.
	• Convert miles to kilometres with a variety of tools and methods.
	• Problem solving involving time zones.
	• Choose units and equipment to measure length.

How you could plan this unit

	Stage 1	Stage 2	Stage 3	Stage 4	Stage 5
Content and vocabulary	Perimeter of rectangles and compound shapes *length, width, centimetre, metre, kilometre, millimetre, perimeter*	Units of length and distance *mile, convert, chart*	Time around the world *Greenwich Mean Time, British Summer Time, International Date Line, time zone*	Choosing units and methods of measuring length *choose, decide, explain your answer, rule, metre stick, tape measure*	
Notes		Resource page A	Resource page B		

Perimeter of rectangles and compound shapes

Oral/mental starter pp 176–177

Advance Organiser

We are going to work out the perimeter – the distance around a shape

---

Whole-class work

- Write on the board: *perimeter*.

- *Who can tell me what perimeter means? Who can describe how we measure the perimeter of a rectangle? Who can describe how to calculate the perimeter of a rectangle?*

- Draw a rectangle on the board and label all the sides, as shown.

- Ask the children to work out the perimeter and record how they did it. Ask the children to show you how they worked it out. Did some work out (length + width) × 2? Did anyone work out (length × 2) + (width × 2)?

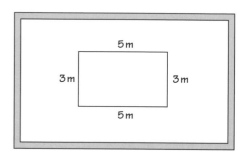

- Discuss which method might be quicker or easier.

- Draw some compound rectangles on the board similar to those shown and mark some of the lengths.

- Discuss how to find the 'missing' dimensions with the children. Ensure that they are clear which measurement belongs with which line. Discuss techniques for working out a missing measurement.

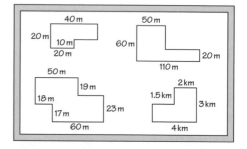

- *What is this distance? How do you know? How did you decide to work it out that way?*

- Work through using subtraction to find one of the measurements.

Independent, paired or group work

- Ask the children to find the missing dimensions of each diagram, then find the perimeter of each one.

- Extend by adding more diagrams, as necessary.

Plenary

- Share the children's results for the compound shapes.

- *Who had anything different? Show me how you worked it out. How can you be sure this measurement is 15 metres?*

Units of length and distance

Advance Organiser

We are going to use different methods to approximate conversions from miles to kilometres

Oral/mental starter
pp 176–177

You will need: resource page A (one per child and one enlarged)

Whole-class work

- Write on the board: *4.8 m.*

- *Who can tell me this length in centimetres? How do you know? Describe how you worked it out.*

- Run through some more decimal conversions of metric units of length.

- Write on the board: $2\frac{1}{2}$ *miles.*

- *How do we convert this to kilometres?*

- Tell the children that a mile is about 1600 metres.

- *How much is this in kilometres?*

- Show the children an enlarged copy of the conversion number line at the top of resource page A.

- *Who can tell me what this shows? How could I use this to convert miles to kilometres, and kilometres to miles? What is 1.6 kilometres in miles? What is 2 miles in kilometres? What is 5 miles in kilometres?*

- Work through various conversions, pointing out that some can be worked out exactly and others must be estimated.

- *Who can show me how to find how many metres in 0.4 kilometres using this chart?*

- Demonstrate using a ruler to find the intersection at 0.4 kilometres.

- *How many miles is 8 kilometres? So how many miles is 16 kilometres? How many kilometres in 20 miles? How can you work it out?*

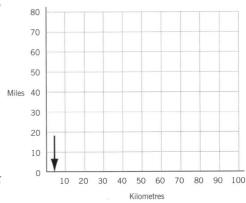

Independent, paired or group work

- Ask the children to complete the questions on resource page A.

- Encourage the children to use the conversion number line, the conversion chart or the calculation method of multiplying by 8 and dividing by 5 and vice versa.

Plenary

- Ask the children to discuss how they worked out each conversion.

- Use a calculator to work out some of the conversions more accurately, using 1.609 kilometres as a closer approximation of 1 mile.

- Discuss how close the children's conversions are to these.

(**PUPIL PAGE**)

Name: _____

Converting miles and kilometres

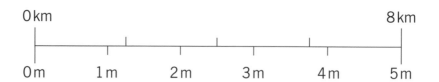

0 km   8 km

0 m   1 m   2 m   3 m   4 m   5 m

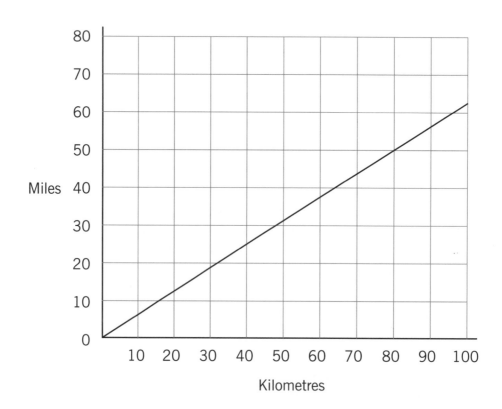

Convert these measurements into different units of length.

1 40 miles is about .... km		**6** 360 km is about .... miles
2 48 km is about .... miles		**7** 125 miles is about .... km
3 65 miles is about .... km		**8** 560 km is about .... miles
4 152 km is about .... miles		**9** 750 miles is about .... km
5 80 miles is about .... km		**10** 960 km is about .... miles

Time around the world

We are going to work out different times around the world

**Oral/mental starter
pp 176–177**

You will need: a globe, a torch, resource page B (one per child and one enlarged)

Whole-class work

- Use the torch to illuminate the globe to illustrate that whilst it is daylight in one part of the world it is dark in another. Make sure you rotate the globe clockwise when viewed from above the North Pole.

- *How long does the earth take to rotate 360 degrees? How do you know?*

- Confirm that it takes 24 hours, one day, for each rotation.

- *When it is midday in London, it is daytime. What time of day will it be in Paris? What about Beijing? What about Sydney?*

- Discuss different areas of the globe and point out that they are in darkness or partly in darkness.

- Ask the children if they know what 'time zones' are. Establish that in different parts of the world people set their clocks to reflect what time of day it is – if it is light when it is midnight in London, they set their clocks accordingly.

- Show the children an enlarged copy of resource page B and talk them through the idea of the time zones, pointing out that when a clock reads 12.00 midday in London, it reads 13.00 in the zone labelled + 1, 14.00 in the zone labelled + 2, and so on.

- *What time is it in San Francisco when it is 12.00 midday in London? How did you work it out?*

- Repeat for some more questions.

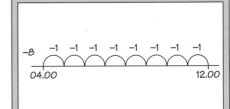

Independent, paired or group work

- Ask the children to complete the problems on resource page B.

Plenary

- Look at questions 16 to 20, whist looking at the globe. Ask the children to position the globe in the correct position for each time by finding where it is midday in each case.

- Discuss the fact that many countries alter the time in another way. For example, in Britain we set our clocks one hour fast in the summer (British Summer Time), in France clocks are two hours fast in summer and one hour fast in winter, and so on.

(**PUPIL PAGE**)

Name: _____

Time around the world

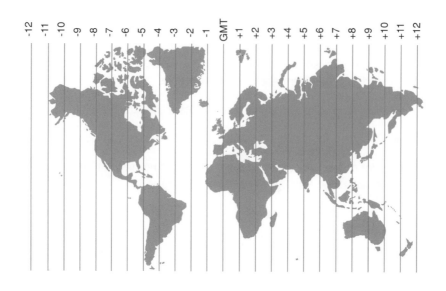

Use 24-hour clock times to complete these sentences.

1 When it is 09.00 in Britain it is .... in France.
2 When it is 13.30 in Britain it is .... on the West coast of the USA.
3 When it is 11.25 in Britain it is .... in Japan.
4 When it is 07.50 in Britain it is .... in New Zealand.
5 When it is 06.45 in Britain it is .... in Jamaica.
6 When it is 20.35 in Britain it is .... in Egypt.
7 When it is 12.55 in Britain it is .... in Australia.
8 When it is 21.20 in Britain it is .... in Argentina.
9 When it is 11.40 in New Zealand it is .... in Britain.
10 When it is 23.55 in Britain it is .... in Honduras.
11 When it is 15.15 in Jamaica it is .... in Britain.
12 When it is 14.28 on the West coast of the USA it is .... in Britain.
13 When it is 21.12 in Britain it is .... in the Falkland Islands.
14 When it is 08.30 in Egypt it is .... in Britain.
15 When it is 07.45 in Australia it is .... in Britain.

Try these. The time goes past midnight so the day changes too.

16 When it is 22.00, Tuesday in Britain it is ...., ... in New Zealand.
17 When it is 02.00, Monday in Britain it is ...., ... on the West coast of the USA.
18 When it is 18.30, Wednesday in Britain it is ...., ... in Japan.
19 When it is 04.15, Sunday in Britain it is ...., ... in Jamaica.
20 When it is 16.40, Friday in Britain it is ...., ... in Australia.

Classworks © Classworks Numeracy author team, Nelson Thornes Ltd, 2003

Choosing units and methods of measuring length

Advance Organiser

We are going to decide which units and methods of measuring are best

Oral/mental starter pp 176–177

You will need: a selection of instruments for measuring length

Whole-class work

- Look at the variety of instruments that you have been able to gather together in the classroom. Write their names on the board.

- Discuss with the children which are more accurate than others and why.

- Ask the children to suggest uses for each of the measuring instruments.

> ruler with mm scale
> metre stick
> tape measure
> surveyor's measuring tape
> trundle wheel

- *What could you measure with a tape measure? Could you measure the length of the playground? What would be a better choice? Why?*

- Discuss different sorts of accuracy, in context and in the real world.

- *Are road signs exactly accurate? Who thinks they could be rounded? What about measurements of clothes? Who can describe when you have to be accurate to the nearest millimetre? Who can describe when you have to be accurate to the nearest metre?*

- Include examples such as designing furniture so that parts fit into other parts, measuring a javelin throw at the Olympics, estimating the surface area of a wall so you can buy enough paint, and so on.

Independent, paired or group work

- Ask the children to write down the five instruments on the board, or other ones they can think of. They should then list several things that each would be more practical than the others for measuring; for example, a ruler could measure a line 12 mm long, the length of a pencil, and so on.

- Stress that answers are not 'right' or 'wrong', they are likely to be 'sensible' and 'practical' or 'difficult to use' and 'awkward'.

Plenary

- Run through the list of things to measure and build up a table on the board of what to measure them with.

- Make a list of any on which there is a split opinion and discuss.

Measures (2)

Outcome

Children will be able to solve problems involving area, mass, profit and loss

Medium-term plan objectives	• Use a formula for the area of a rectangle.
	• Calculate the area of a shape formed from rectangles, including using a calculator with memory.
	• Use, read and write standard metric units of mass, including abbreviations, and relationships.
	• Convert larger to smaller units of mass and vice versa.
	• Know approximate metric equivalents for pounds and ounces.
	• Suggest suitable units and equipment to estimate or measure mass.
	• Record estimates/measurements from scales to a suitable degree of accuracy.
	• Use all four operations to solve measurement word problems.
	• Choose appropriate operations/calculation methods.
	• Explain working.
Overview	• Calculate the area of rectangles and composite shapes.
	• Convert metric units of mass.
	• Introduce and convert imperial units of mass.
	• Problems with mass based on a school scenario.

How you could plan this unit

	Stage 1	Stage 2	Stage 3	Stage 4	Stage 5
Content and vocabulary	Area of compound rectangles *area, covers, surface, square centimetre, square metre, square millimetre*	Grams, kilograms and tonnes *tonne, kilogram, half kilogram, gram*	Imperial and metric units of mass *pound, ounce*	Solving problems involving maths *profit, loss*	
Notes	Resource page A		Resource page B		

100

Area of compound rectangles

Advance Organiser

We are going to use calculators to work out the area of the classroom and the playground

Oral/mental starter pp 176–177

You will need: calculators, 4-metre sticks taped together to form a square metre, resource page A (one per child)

Whole-class work

- Lay the square metre on the floor and ask the children if they know what it is.
- *How do you know? What does this measure? Why is it called a square metre?*
- Establish that it is one metre in length and one metre in breadth, making it a square, and that it is a unit for measuring area.
- *How many children can fit within it without overhanging? Make a good guess or estimate. Who thinks more can fit in? Who thinks fewer?*
- Compare the result to their estimates.
- Draw out a plan of the classroom floor, based upon an approximation of length and width in whole metres.
- *How could we find the area of this plan of our classroom?*
- Take ideas from the children. Draw square metres on the plan and demonstrate counting.
- *How could we calculate the area?*
- Revise the fact that the area of a rectangle is found by multiplying the length by the breadth. Try a couple of examples.
- Look for the suggestion that the plan of the classroom could be split into rectangles.
- Demonstrate, or ask a child to do so.
- Work through finding the area of the individual rectangles, asking the children to describe each stage.

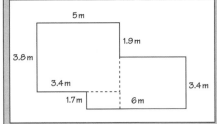

Independent, paired or group work

- Ask the children to complete resource page A.
- If they have time after completing the sheet, they can design a rectangle-composite playground sheet for a partner to calculate.

Plenary

- Look at the composite shapes. How did the children divide them up?
- How many ways were there?
- Show an alternative method – 'round up' the shape to a large rectangle and subtract the area(s) which have been included which should not be there. For example:

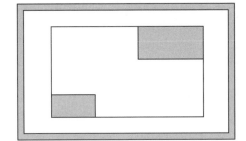

Name: _____

Working out area

Find the area of these playgrounds.

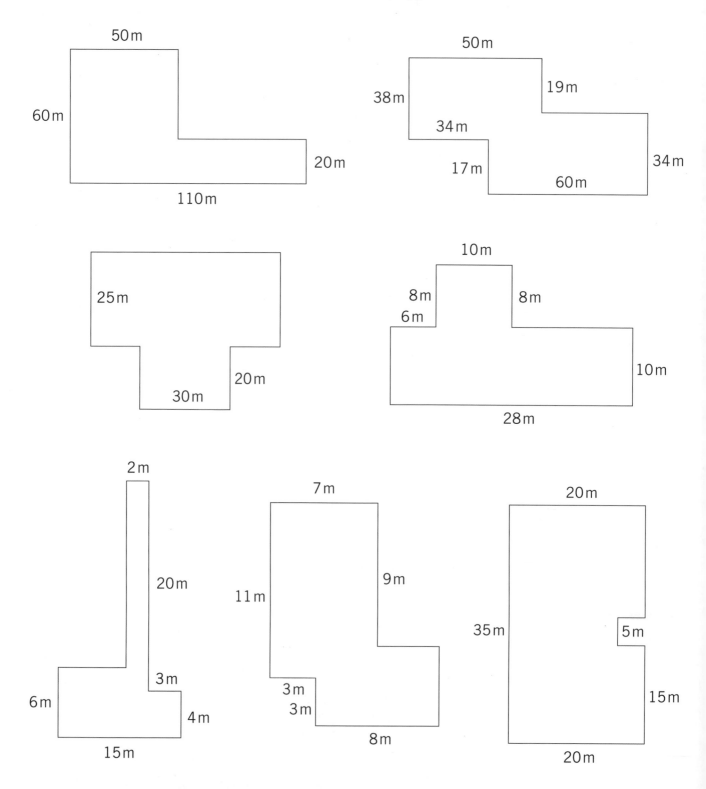

Grams, kilograms and tonnes

Advance Organiser

We are going to compare and convert metric units of mass

Oral/mental starter pp 176–177

Whole-class work

- Write on the board: *kilogram* and *gram*.

- Ask the children to tell you what they know about each one and the relationship between them.

- Remind them that *kilo*gram means *thousand* gram(*s*). Often people abbreviate kilogram to kilo.

- *How do I convert an amount of kilograms to an equivalent amount of grams?*

- Try some examples, demonstrating, if necessary, on the board how this can be done easily by multiplying or dividing by 1000 (shifting digits three columns to the left or right).

- Stress the necessity to insert any place-holding zeros.

- Introduce the metric tonne as being 1000 kg. For reference, a family car weighs about one metric tonne.

- Write some mass measures in kilograms (with decimal values) on the board.

- Demonstrate how to round them up or down to the nearest whole kilogram (if the tenths column is 5 or more – round up, otherwise – round down).

- Show how to round tonnes up or down to the nearest whole, in exactly the same way.

- *How many grams in half a kilogram? How do you know? How many kilograms in three-quarters of a metric tonne? How do you know? What is 30% of 2 kilograms? How did you work it out?*

- Encourage the children to use different methods to solve each conversion, including using mental, written or calculator methods.

Independent, paired or group work

- Ask the children to write conversion problems for each other involving kilograms, grams and metric tonnes. They should write three involving fractions, three involving percentages and three involving decimals.

- Ask them to answer their own questions on a separate piece of paper, then swap them with a partner.

Plenary

- Compare the children's answers. Ask them to check other pairs' answers and compare methods.

- Ask the children to challenge the rest of the class to solve their problems.

- Discuss real-life contexts for unit conversion and ask the children to invent story problems.

Imperial and metric units of mass

Advance Organiser

We are going to convert measurements of mass in imperial units to equivalent metric units

Oral/mental starter pp 176–177

You will need: balances with metric and imperial units of weight, resource page B (one per child and one enlarged)

Whole-class work

- Write on the board: *mass, pound, lb, ounce* and *oz.*

- *Who has heard or seen these units before? Who can tell me what they are called?*

- Revise or tell the children some approximate conversions, both from one imperial unit to another and from metric to imperial and vice versa.

- *There are 16 ounces in 1 pound.*

- *A pound weighs about the same as a glass of water. It is approximately 450 g, a little less than half a kilogram.*

- *An ounce weighs about the same as a packet of crisps. It is about 28 g but we often round this up to 30 g to make it easier to convert.*

- *A kilogram is about 2.2 pounds or about the same as 36 ounces.*

- *Half a kilogram is just a little more than a pound, about $1\frac{1}{10}$ pounds.*

- Discuss how you could convert pounds to kilograms, grams to ounces, and so on.

- Introduce, if necessary, the idea of a conversion graph. Show the children an enlarged copy of resource page B and ask them to describe how it can be used to convert between units.

- Work through some examples, demonstrating how to find a mass along one axis and find its equivalent along the other.

Independent, paired or group work

- Ask the children to complete resource page B.

- They can use the conversion charts or, alternatively, one of the calculation methods.

Plenary

- Discuss whether there are some easy approximations (for example, $\frac{1}{2}$ kg is just over 1 pound, 100 g is just under $\frac{1}{4}$ lb/4oz).

- Ask the children to suggest things that weigh about an ounce, about half a pound, and so on.

- Discuss the advantages and disadvantages of the metric and imperial systems.

- *How many ounces in a quarter of a pound? How many grams in a quarter of a kilo?*

- *How many ounces in half a pound? How many grams in half a kilo?*

- *How many ounces in two and a quarter pounds? Is that easier or harder, than the number of grams in two and a quarter kilos?*

(**PUPIL PAGE**)

Name: _____

Converting imperial and metric units

- 1 pound (1lb) is about 450g, 0.450kg
- 1 ounce (1oz) is about 30g
- 1 kilogram is about 2.2 pounds
- $\frac{1}{2}$ kilogram is about 1.1lb, just over 1 pound

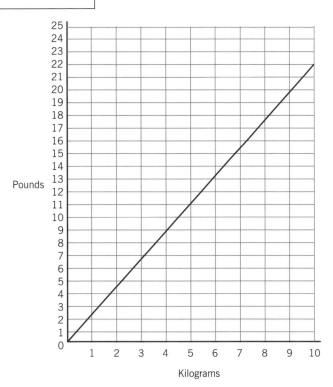

Convert these measures of mass using the resources above.

1 2 kg is about .... lb

2 2 lb is about .... g

3 5 oz is about .... g

4 300 g is about .... oz

5 10 kg is about .... lb

6 4 lb is about .... kg

7 500 g is about .... lb

8 10 oz is about .... g

9 0.750 kg is about .... oz

10 16 oz is about .... kg

11 20 oz = ... lb, ... oz

12 25 oz = ... lb, ... oz

13 60 oz = ... lb, ... oz

14 72 oz = ... lb, ... oz

Classworks © Classworks Numeracy author team, Nelson Thornes Ltd, 2003

Solving problems involving maths

Advance Organiser

We are going to use our maths skills to work out the figures for a small business

---

Whole-class work

- Write the following scenario on the board. Ask the children to read it carefully and listen while you read it out.

- Ask the children how they think the business will try to make money. Discuss real-life situations, including the fact that large amounts of things are often better value than small amounts.

> Year 6 at Priory School is running a business enterprise. They buy large bags of Bombay mix to re-package it in smaller amounts to sell at playtime.
>
> They buy a 10lb bag from a wholesaler costing £7.20. They want to sell Bombay mix in 75g portions.

- Ask the children what else they might need to buy in order to sell the Bombay mix.

- Ask the children to discuss what price they could sell the 75g bags of mix at. Introduce the terms *profit* and *loss*.

- Work through finding the cost of each small bag, including the mix and the sandwich bag. Encourage the children to discuss how to find these costs.

> They need to buy sandwich bags and ties. A pack of 50 of each costs 95p.
>
> How many small bags would they get from every large bag? If they sold every small bag for 25p, how much profit would they make overall?

- Discuss alternative situations.

- *What if Bombay mix only cost 22p per bag in the local shop? How much can they charge and still make a profit? How will they tell people that they are selling Bombay mix? How much would that cost? What if they only sold three-quarters of the large bag and the rest went stale?*

Independent, paired or group work

- Ask the children to use the information above and to think of, or find out, other information as necessary. Encourage them to decide what might happen and whether this would be a money-making business or not.

Plenary

- Discuss what the children decided. Ask groups of children to present their businesses to the class.

Measures (3)

Outcome

Children will be able to approximate capacities, convert between units and solve word problems involving capacity

Medium-term plan objectives	• Use, read and write metric units of capacity, including abbreviations and relationships.
	• Convert larger to smaller units of capacity, and vice versa.
	• Know approximate metric equivalents for pint and gallon.
	• Suggest suitable units and equipment to estimate or measure capacity.
	• Record estimates/measurements from scales to a suitable degree of accuracy.
	• Use all four operations to solve measurement word problems.
	• Choose appropriate operations/calculation methods.
	• Explain working.
Overview	• Convert metric units of capacity.
	• Convert metric and imperial units.
	• Problems with capacity based on a school scenario.

How you could plan this unit

	Stage 1	Stage 2	Stage 3	Stage 4	Stage 5
Content and vocabulary	Investigating capacity *capacity, full, half full, empty, holds, contains, litre, half litre, centilitre, millilitre*	Pints, gallons and litres *pint, gallon*	Capacity word problems *tell me, describe, explain your reasoning*		
Notes		Resource page A	Resource page B		

Investigating capacity

Advance Organiser

We are going to make a millilitre measure using a centimetre cube

Oral/mental starter pp 176–177

You will need: litre pop bottle(s) or other litre containers, centicube, plasticine

Whole-class work

- Show the children a litre container.

- *How many millilitres will this container hold? How do you know?*

- Show the children a centimetre cube.

- *I am going to push this centimetre cube into the plasticine. What will happen? Who can describe it to me? What do you think will be the capacity of the space it leaves in the plasticine? Why do you think that?*

- Press the cube into a blob of plasticine and carefully remove it.

- Demonstrate filling a narrow measuring cylinder with the cube and discuss what you found.

- Work through finding the capacity of the space left by the cube.

- Ask the children to suggest other shapes in the class that could be turned into containers.

- Show the children a variety of litre containers.

- *All of these have a capacity of about 1 litre. Who thinks I am correct? Who knows how we can find out?*

- Stress that whilst the shape of each container may differ, their capacity does not.

- Pour a litre of water into different-shaped litre containers to prove the point.

Independent, paired or group work

- Ask the children to choose a selection of small objects such as marbles, beads, centicubes, counters, and so on.

- They should press them into plasticine and compare how much each impression holds by filling one from the other.

Plenary

- Discuss the children's findings.

- *Who was surprised? What did you find out?*

- Ask the children to discuss the amount of space taken up by the different objects.

- Include 3-D shapes such as rectangles. Ask the children to imagine a cube as a box and then taking the lid off the box. How much would it hold inside? If possible, illustrate using Polydron or Clixi or similar.

Pints, gallons and litres

Advance Organiser

We are going to compare capacity measured in imperial and metric measures

Oral/mental starter
pp 176–177

You will need: resource page A (one per child and one enlarged)

Whole-class work

- Write on the board: *pint* and *gallon*.

- *Who can tell me what these mean? Where have you heard or seen them before? About how many litres are in 1 pint? How many litres in a gallon, approximately?*

- Remind the children that the pint and gallon are part of the imperial system of measures and they do not easily convert to metric units.

- Tell them that 1 gallon (8 pints) is close to 4.54609 litres and 1 pint is around 0.56826 litres.

- *Is it easy to use these conversions? How could we make it easier to convert gallons and pints to litres?*

- Encourage the children to suggest approximations. Write some on the board.

- Discuss how to convert the measurements.

- Show the children the conversion graph at the top of resource page A.

- *How can this help? Who can show me how to use this?*

> 1 litre is about $1\frac{3}{4}$ pints (1·75 pints)
>
> 1 pint is about $\frac{6}{10}$ of a litre (0·6 litre)
>
> 1 gallon is about $4\frac{1}{2}$ litres (4·5 litres)
>
> 1 litre is about $\frac{1}{5}$ of a gallon (0·22 to be more accurate)

- Encourage the children to measure along the line and read off various conversions.

- Ask the class to check using a calculator. Discuss how close the conversions are each time.

Independent, paired or group work

- Ask the children to complete the conversions on resource page A and check them using a calculator. Alternatively they can approximate, based on the information shown above.

Plenary

- Select a few of the conversions and work them out, first using the approximation and then using a calculator to work them out more accurately.

- *To convert litres to pints, divide by 0.5682624.*

- *To convert pints to litres, multiply by 0.5682624.*

- *To convert litres to gallons, divide by 4.546099.*

- *To convert gallons to litres, multiply by 4.546099.*

- Discuss how close the approximations are. Would the margin of error make much difference for most purposes?

Name: _____

Metric and imperial capacity

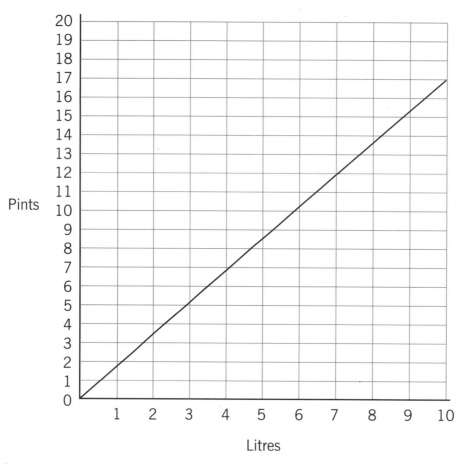

Complete these conversions:

1	3 gallons is about	.... litres	**13**	36 pints is about	.... litres
2	8 litres is about	.... pints	**14**	4 gallons is about	.... litres
3	10 litres is about	.... gallons	**15**	10 gallons is about	.... litres
4	10 pints is about	.... litres	**16**	28 pints is about	.... litres
5	12 litres is about	.... pints	**17**	18 pints is about	.... litres
6	8 litres is about	.... gallons	**18**	20 litres is about	.... pints
7	16 pints is about	.... litres	**19**	14 gallons is about	.... litres
8	6 gallons is about	.... litres	**20**	44 litres is about	.... gallons
9	14 litres is about	.... gallons	**21**	15 pints is about	.... litres
10	4 litres is about	.... pints	**22**	25 litres is about	.... pints
11	15 litres is about	.... pints	**23**	25 litres is about	.... gallons
12	22 litres is about	.... gallons	**24**	7 gallons is about	.... litres

Capacity word problems

Advance Organiser

We are going to choose the best way to work out some word problems

Oral/mental starter pp 176–177

You will need: calculators, resource page B (one per child and one enlarged)

Whole-class work

- Read through the problem at the top of the enlarged version of resource page B a couple of times.

- Discuss the importance of breaking the problem down into stages, writing down what each stage is and how to work it out.

- Ask the children to visualise what is happening and to think of what they know and what they need to find out. Prompt them with questions and discuss different methods.

- *How much paint of each colour does each class need? How do we find that out? How many tins should they buy? How did you work that out?*

- Encourage the children to use mental, written or calculator methods for each stage, as appropriate.

- *How could you work that out? Would you need to use a calculator? Could you do it quicker without one? How would you check you were right?*

- Stress the importance of writing down each stage, including what was keyed into the calculator, the answers from the calculator, and what the answers represent.

Independent, paired or group work

- Ask the children to complete resource page B, recording their working-out and their finished answers in their books.

Plenary

- Work through the problems together.

- Discuss if it would have been cheaper to buy more expensive paint that only required one coat per room.

- Ask the children to discuss other ways of solving the problems and check various stages with the children.

Name: _____

Word problems

Solve these problems and show your working-out in your book. If you use a calculator, write down what you did so you can check your answer.

The head teacher wanted the caretaker to paint all 6 classrooms during the school holidays. Having measured up, she knows that in each room there is 65m² of wall and 45m² of ceiling to be painted. She chose BotchIt DIY's own-brand paint, because it was the cheapest and it said on the tin that a 5 litre can covers 50m². There were only two colours, so she bought grey for the walls and white for the ceilings.

1   How many litres of white paint were needed for each classroom?
2   How many litres of grey paint were needed for each classroom?
3   How many litres of white paint were needed to give one coat of paint to all the classrooms?
4   How many litres of grey paint were needed to give one coat of paint to all the classrooms?
5   BotchIt DIY's own-brand paint only comes in 5 litre tins. How many tins of each colour did they need to buy?
6   How much paint of each colour was left over when the caretaker finished?

When the job was complete, the head teacher could tell why the paint was so cheap. It was so thin that everywhere needed a second coat.

7   How much more white paint is needed?
8   How many more 5 litre tins of white paint had to be bought?
9   How much white paint was left over?
10 How much more grey paint is needed?
11 How many more 5 litre tins or grey paint had to be bought?
12 How much grey paint was left over?

Painting the school in the summer holidays was very thirsty work. Every time that he poured a litre of paint into the paint roller tray he drank half a glass of lemonade. A full glass held 300ml.

13 How many roller trays of paint did he need to give 1 coat of paint to 1 classroom?
14 How many 300ml glasses of lemonade did he drink each time he painted a classroom?
15 How many litres of lemonade did he drink each time he painted a classroom?
16 The caretaker painted 6 classrooms twice. How many litres of lemonade did he drink altogether?
17 How many 3 litre bottles did he buy?
18 How many millilitres of lemonade were left in the last bottle?

Classworks © Classworks Numeracy author team, Nelson Thornes Ltd, 2003

Shape and Space (1)

Outcome

Children will be able to use what they know about shape and space to classify and explore the properties of shapes, and use coordinates to describe translations

Medium-term plan objectives

- Classify quadrilaterals using side/angle properties.
- Read and plot coordinates in all four quadrants.
- Recognise where a shape will be after two translations.
- Solve shape puzzles.
- Explain methods and reasoning orally, and in writing.

Overview

- Consolidate work on angles in triangles.
- Classify quadrilaterals using sides and angles.
- Plot coordinates in all four quadrants.
- Solve a shape puzzle: does every quadrilateral tessellate?

How you could plan this unit

	Stage 1	Stage 2	Stage 3	Stage 4	Stage 5	Stage 6	Stage 7
Content and vocabulary	Exploring triangles in polygons *straight, centre, intersecting, intersection, triangle, polygon, square, pentagon, hexagon, heptagon, octagon*	Classifying quadrilaterals *angle, right-angled, regular, irregular*	Revising plotting coordinates in one quadrant	Plotting coordinates in four quadrants *grid, row, column, quadrant, x-axis, y-axis, origin, coordinates, translation*	Consolidating two translations in four quadrants	Revising names and properties of 3-D shapes, or revise as required	Tessellation *congruent, tessellate*
	Resource page A						
Notes							

113

Exploring triangles in polygons

Advance Organiser

We are going to use what we know about triangles and regular polygons to predict the size of angles

Oral/mental starter pp 177–179

You will need: protractors, rulers, resource page A (one per child and one enlarged)

Whole-class work

- Show the children an enlarged copy of resource page A. Point to the square.

- *What is the name of this shape? How has it been divided up?*

- Confirm that the shape is a square and that it has been divided up into triangles. Point out that the triangles all meet at the centre of the square.

- *I can find out how many degrees there are in each angle of each triangle without using a protractor. How can I do that?*

- Discuss some ideas and write them on the board. Lead the children through the following process, discussing what they think at each point.

- *How many degrees are there in a complete turn? What can you say about these triangles?*

- Demonstrate that the triangles are identical by cutting them out and fitting them over each other.

- *So, how many angles in each one?*

- Talk through dividing 360 by the number of angles at the centre as shown above.

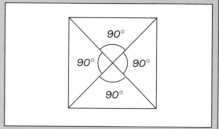

- *How do we find out the other angles of the triangle? What sort of triangle is it?*

- Lead the children towards the idea that they know the outside shape is a square and that the triangles join at the centre of the square. Each triangle must be isosceles as two of its sides are half of a diagonal. Point out that it cannot be equilateral because the angle at the centre is 90 degrees, not 60 degrees.

- Ask someone to work out the size of the other two angles in each triangle. Ask them to explain their reasoning.

- Check with a protractor.

Independent, paired or group work

- Ask the children to complete resource page A in pairs.

Plenary

- *Which shape had isosceles triangles? Which had equilateral triangles? How can you be sure? Which shape had right-angled triangles? Why were there no scalene triangles?*

- Check that everyone understands how the angles at the centre of the polygon were calculated.

Name: _____

Exploring triangles in polygons

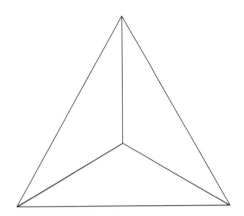
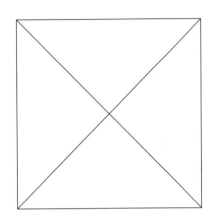
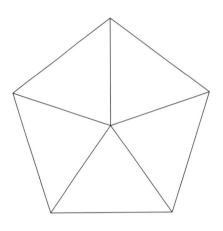

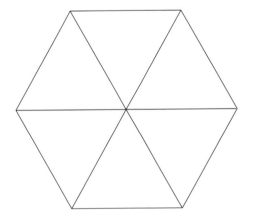
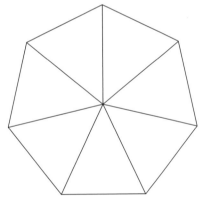
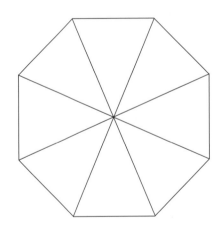

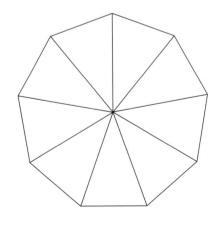
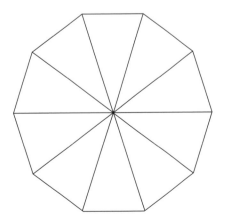

Classifying quadrilaterals

Advance Organiser

We are going to revise the names of quadrilaterals and sort them out in different ways

Oral/mental starter pp 177–179

You will need: pencils, paper

Whole-class work

- Write on the board: *quadrilaterals*.
- Ask the children to explain what it means.
- Brainstorm the names of shapes that are quadrilaterals and write them on the board.
- Discuss how they are similar and different. Encourage the children to use appropriate vocabulary.
- Discuss sorting the names into sets using these criteria: right-angles/no right-angles, at least one pair of sides parallel/no sides parallel, opposite sides of equal length/opposite sides not equal, diagonals intersect at right-angles/diagonals do not intersect at right-angles.
- Discuss the difficulty concerning some shapes which can *sometimes* have one property; for example, a parallelogram has right angles when it is a rectangle; a rectangle has diagonals that intersect at right angles when it is a square, and so on.
- If the children are not sure which set a shape belongs to, draw the shape to check.
- *Does any shape fit into every 'no not' category?*

Independent, paired or group work

- Ask the children to use a Carroll or a Venn diagram to sort the shapes.
- Suggest categories, or let children choose their own. Encourage them to watch out for shapes that *sometimes* possess a property and *sometimes* do not. How can they sort those shapes?

	Quadrilaterals with a right-angle	Quadrilaterals without a right-angle
Quadrilaterals with sides parallel		
Quadrilaterals with sides not parallel		

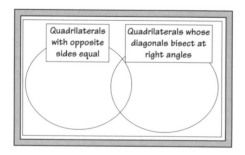

Plenary

- Ask different children to explain why they have placed a particular shape in a given category. Check that shapes are correctly placed in both diagrams.
- Discuss different ways of sorting – how are the shapes grouped by different children?
- *Are some shapes always or almost always in the same set as each other? Are some shapes never or rarely in the same set as each other? Why do you think that is?*

Plotting coordinates in four quadrants

Advance Organiser

We are going to use four quadrants to plot coordinates

Oral/mental starter pp 177–179

You will need: squared paper, pencils, rulers

Whole-class work

- Show the children how to use squared paper to draw and label the four quadrants.

- Ask the children to describe the grids. Encourage them to use the appropriate vocabulary.

- *Why do we call this section a quadrant? How many are there on the whole grid? What else has the word 'quad' in?*

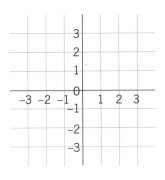

- Look for the following characteristics. The first quadrant is numbered with positive numbers. The second quadrant is negative on the horizontal (x) axis and positive on the vertical (y) axis. The third quadrant has negative numbers in both directions. The fourth quadrant has a positive horizontal (x) axis and a negative vertical (y) axis.

- Ask the children to describe how to find points in each quadrant; for example, $(2, 3)$ $(2, -3)$ $(-2, -3)$ and $(-2, 3)$. Ask some children to the board to choose a point and ask the class to say its coordinates.

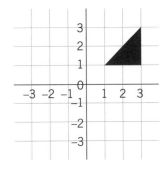

- Draw a simple shape in the grid such as the one in the diagram. Work out the coordinates for the corners if the shape is moved four units down and one unit left.

Independent, paired or group work

- Ask the children to use squared paper to draw the grid with four quadrants.

- They should label the grid -5 to 5 along both axes. They then shade in a triangle in one quadrant. Tell them to decide upon two moves for the triangle and to describe that move, giving a direction and number of units; for example, left three units, down three units.

- They then write the coordinates of the corners of the triangle before and after two moves.

Plenary

- Ask the children to express the two translations for their shape, and the coordinates they began and ended with.

- Check the coordinates and translation with the class each time.

Tessellation

Advance Organiser

We are going to find out if you can use any type of quadrilateral as a tile

Oral/mental starter pp 177–179

You will need: thin card, pencils, rulers, scissors, 2-D shapes to draw around

Whole-class work

- Write on the board: *tessellate*.
- *Who can tell me what this means?*
- *What shapes tessellate on their own? Can you make a tessellation using just circles? Why not? What about triangles?*
- Ask some children to the front of the class to demonstrate drawing around 2-D shapes to make some patterns with equilateral, isosceles and right-angled triangles.
- *Do they leave any gaps?*
- *What about scalene triangles? Is it possible to predict whether shapes will tessellate?*
- *How could we do that? How do you know?*
- Encourage statements along the lines of *you can make straight lines with squares so they will tessellate*, or *triangles that have all sides the same length tessellate because the sides match*, or *right-angled triangles tessellate because you can make squares from them.*

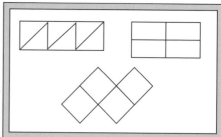

- Make a list of quadrilaterals. Ask the class to suggest which will tessellate. Put a cross beside those that they predict will leave gaps.
- *Why do you think that? Does anyone else think any differently?*

Independent, paired or group work

- Ask the children in each group to decide which quadrilateral each person will investigate.
- *Carefully draw your quadrilateral, or use a template. Draw around your card shape.*
- *Experiment with the shape to see if you can make a tessellating pattern with no gaps.*
- *Draw around your shape about eight times.*
- *Write a statement saying whether your shape tessellates.*
- *Write another sentence or two explaining why you think this is so.*

Plenary

- Check the patterns against the predictions.
- *Were the predictions correct? Were there any surprises?*
- Compare results from different groups.
- *Did some people manage to draw tessellations with a shape where others found gaps? Why was this?*
- *Can you make a statement about quadrilaterals and tessellations? Can you give a reason for it?*

Shape and Space (2)

Outcome

Children will be able to visualise and predict 2-D and 3-D shapes and patterns from drawings and what they know about shape and space

Medium-term plan objectives	• Make shapes with increasing accuracy. • Visualise 3-D shapes from 2-D drawings. • Identify nets for a closed cube. • Recognise and estimate acute and obtuse angles. • Use a protractor to measure and draw acute/obtuse angles to 1 degree. • Check the angle sum of a triangle is 180 degrees. • Calculate angles in a triangle or around a point. • Recognise where a shape will be after 90 degree rotation about a vertex. • Recognise and explain patterns and relationships, generalise and predict.
Overview	• Hexominoes and nets for a closed cube. • Visualise 3-D shapes from 2-D drawings. • Check the angle sum of a triangle is 180 degrees. • Recognise where a shape will be after 90 degree rotation about a vertex. • Recognise and explain patterns and relationships, generalise and predict.

How you could plan this unit

	Stage 1	Stage 2	Stage 3	Stage 4	Stage 5
	Nets for closed cubes	Visualising a 3-D shape from 2-D drawings	Checking the angle sum of triangles	90 degree rotations about a vertex	Recognising and explaining patterns
Content and vocabulary	*net, make, build, cube, predict*	*imagine, three-dimensional, two-dimensional*	*angle, straight line, degree*	*whole turn, half turn, quarter turn, rotate, rotation*	*translation, reflection, pattern, repeating pattern*
Notes					Resource page A

Nets for closed cubes

Advance Organiser

We are going to make a net of a closed cube and number it like a die

**Oral/mental starter
pp 177–179**

You will need: 2 cm squared paper, scissors, pencils, 1 to 6 die

Whole-class work

- Use a large sheet of 2 cm squared paper. Ask someone to outline six adjoining squares. Ask the children to predict whether it can be folded into a closed cube.

- *Which square would be at the top of the cube? Which would be at the bottom? How do you know?*

- Repeat until you have one of the nets of a closed cube and cut it out.

- Show the children a 1 to 6 die and pass it around the class. Point out which numbers are opposite each other.

- *What can you say about these pairs of numbers?*

- *Where could I write the numbers 1 to 6 on this net so it folded into a die like this one? Who can help me make a prediction?*

- Ask the children to give you suggestions for writing numbers inside the squares of your net, predicting which faces will be opposite each other when the shape is folded into a cube, and trying to make pairs of opposite numbers add to 7.

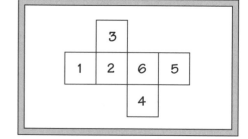

- Cut out and fold the net. Compare the numbering with the die.

- *Does this match our die?*

- Repeat, asking the children to help you predict and draw the shape of a different net that will make a cube. Write the numbers in the same way. Check by cutting and folding the cube.

Independent, paired or group work

- Ask the children to use squared paper to draw as many different arrangements of six squares as they can. They should predict which will fold to make closed cubes, and write numbers on those cubes to resemble a 1 to 6 die.

- Ask them to use scissors to cut out and test their predictions.

Plenary

- Draw on the board the total number of different arrangements of squares discovered as the children suggest them.

- *How many could be folded into cubes? How many could not?*

- *Can anyone make a statement about the ones that can or cannot be folded into a cube?*

Visualising 3-D shapes from 2-D drawings

Advance Organiser

We are going to use plan and elevation drawings to predict and build three-dimensional shapes

Oral/mental starter pp 177–179

You will need: pencils, paper, linking cubes, squared paper

Whole-class work

- Show the children this plan (view from above) and elevation (view from the side) and three-dimensional drawing.

- *How many cubes will be needed to make this pattern? Why do you think that?*

- Challenge the children to use cubes to make the shape. Discuss how many cubes they will need.

- Demonstrate the top and side views. Check the three-dimensional drawing.

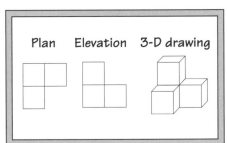

- *Why can only three cubes be seen in each view? How did you decide you needed four cubes to make the shape?*

- Ask someone to make a different shape with four cubes. Draw the view from above. Draw the view from the side. Check the shape against each viewpoint.

- Ask a volunteer to draw a three-dimensional drawing of the shape, or draw it yourself.

Independent, paired or group work

- Ask everyone to take four or five cubes.

- They fit the cubes together to make a shape, then draw the top and side views. Allow the children to use squared paper if it is easier. They can attempt a 3-D drawing if they wish.

- *Make and draw at least two more shapes with your cubes. Record two views of each shape.*

Plenary

- Choose one of the top and side views and ask someone else to make the shape.

- Check the shape against the drawings.

- Look at any three-dimensional drawings with the class.

- Predict the number of cubes needed, then make the shape.

- Check it against the top and side views.

Checking the angle sum of triangles

Advance Organiser

We are going to check that the sum of the angles in a triangle is 180 degrees

Oral/mental starter
pp 177–179

You will need: paper, pencils, scissors, glue, protractors, rulers

Whole-class work

- Cut any triangle from a piece of paper. Put a dot in each corner and cut or tear off the three angles.

- *Who can help me make a straight line from these three angles? Who thinks it is possible? Who thinks it is not possible?*

- Ask someone to arrange the three angles in a straight line.

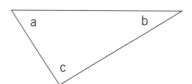 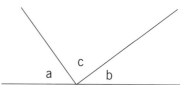

- *Who can explain why this happens?*

- *What do we know about angles in a straight line?*

- *Will this work for all kinds of triangles?*

- With the class, discuss what will happen with equilateral, isosceles and right-angled triangles.

Independent, paired or group work

- Ask the children to use a protractor and a ruler to draw one equilateral triangle, one scalene triangle and one isosceles triangle.

- Then they write the number of degrees inside each angle.

- Ask them to tear off the corners of each triangle.

- Next, they arrange and glue them along a line as shown above.

- Finally, they write a number sentence, adding the number of degrees in each angle for each straight line.

Plenary

- Discuss all the triangles.

- *Did any have three angles that did not add up to 180 degrees? Why was that?*

- Draw a square with both diagonals.

- *Who can write in the size of an angle? How do you know?*

90 degree rotations about a vertex

Advance Organiser

We are going to rotate shapes through 90 degrees

You will need: paper, pencils, rulers, compasses or templates to draw circles

Whole-class work

- Draw some shapes like these on the board. Draw a shape inside one segment; for example, a crescent. (The shape should have only one line of symmetry, or be asymmetrical. If it has two lines of symmetry it will not change when rotated through 90 degrees.)

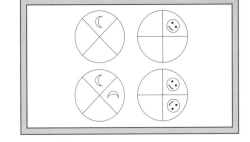

- Ask someone to draw the crescent in the next segment, turned through 90 degrees.

- *How did you decide that? Who thinks anything different? How can we find out how the shape will look?*

- If necessary, demonstrate using cut-out shapes.

- Ask other children to help you complete the other two segments for another turn of 90 degrees.

- Discuss each time what happens to the shape.

Independent, paired or group work

- Ask the children to devise a shape and draw it inside one quarter of each of these designs.

- Give your designs to a partner to complete by rotating each quarter through 90 degrees. Return the designs to the first person and check they are correct.

Plenary

- Discuss patterns which were easy or difficult to rotate.

- *Is a symmetrical shape easier or harder to rotate? Describe how symmetrical shapes like this change when rotated. What do you notice?*

- Discuss how the shapes inside the segments change after each rotation.

Recognising and explaining patterns

Advance Organiser

We are going to experiment with tile patterns, using translations, reflections and rotations to make regular patterns

Oral/mental starter pp 177–179

You will need: coloured pencils, scissors, Blu-Tack, resource page A (one per child)

Whole-class work

- Using tiles cut out from resource page A, or larger paper squares divided by a single diagonal and shaded on one side, ask questions about the patterns made by arranging them in different relationships.

- *Who knows what a horizontal translation means? Who can describe it? How far shall we translate the pattern? What if we translate the pattern one square along? What would it look like?*

- Discuss possible patterns and ask someone to draw what they think will happen.

- Ask someone else to rearrange the squares so that pairs reflect each other.

- Then rearrange the squares so that they rotate through 90 degrees each time.

- Discuss the way the pattern changes.

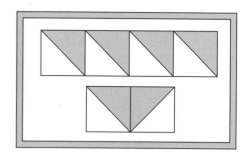

Independent, paired or group work

- Ask the children to colour and cut out the larger tiles from resource page A to experiment with patterns. They shade one half of each tile, using the same colour throughout.

- *Each time you devise a pattern, record it in a block of 16 tiles on one of the grids.*

- *Write the instructions for making each pattern in terms of translation, reflection and rotation.*

- Encourage the children to make regular patterns – patterns that are predictable.

- *How many regular patterns can be created?*

- *Can you change the instructions for your pattern? Can you predict what will happen to the pattern?*

- Some children could develop this work on the computer.

Plenary

- Discuss the patterns. Check that each pattern is regular (predictable).

- *Does each pattern match the instructions that have been written for it?*

- *How many regular patterns have been devised?*

- *What kind of design would produce different patterns in the same way?*

(CUT-OUT)

Tile patterns

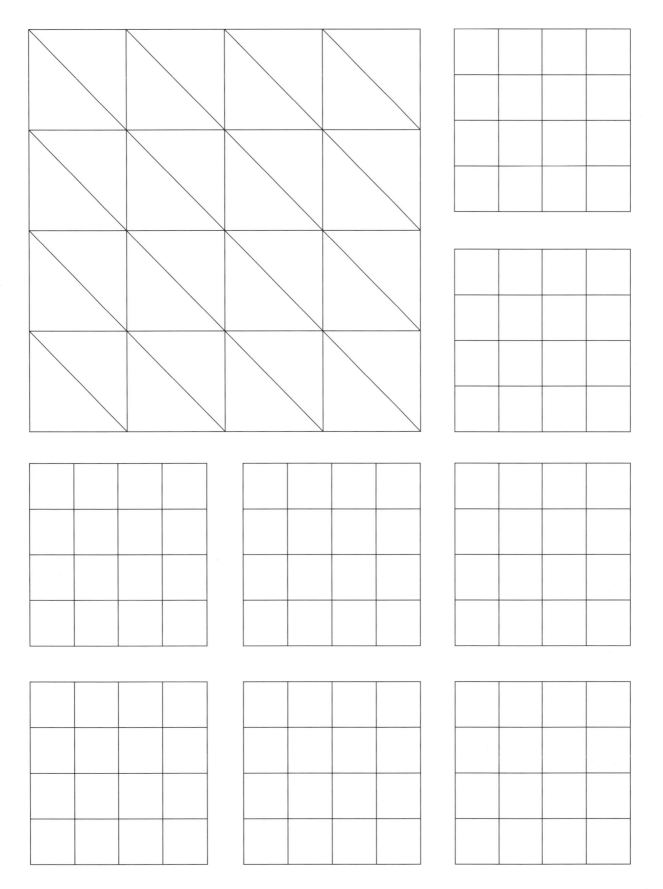

Shape and Space (3)

Outcome

Children will be able to predict positions of shapes after translations and reflections, and investigate a statement about congruent triangles

Medium-term plan objectives

- Recognise where a shape will be after reflection in a line not parallel to a side.
- Draw a shape reflected in two mirrors at 90 degrees.
- Consolidate work on translations and rotations.
- Make and investigate a general statement about shapes.

Overview

- Recognise where a shape will be after reflection in a line not parallel to a side.
- Draw a shape reflected in two mirrors at 90 degrees.
- Consolidate work on translations and rotations.
- Make and investigate a definition for congruent triangles.

How you could plan this unit

	Stage 1	Stage 2	Stage 3	Stage 4	Stage 5	Stage 6	Stage 7
Content and vocabulary	Revising names, definitions and features of polyhedra	Predicting a reflected shape *reflection, mirror line, reflect, parallel*	Shapes reflected in mirrors at 90 degrees	Revising translations in four quadrants	Making reflections using four quadrants *quadrant, coordinates, grid, translations*	Revising names, definitions and features of polygons	Finding definitions for congruent triangles *triangle, congruent*
Notes							

126

Predicting a reflected shape

Advance Organiser

We are going to predict where shapes will be when reflected in a line not parallel to a side

You will need: pencils, paper, mirrors, protractors

Whole-class work

- Use capital letters with straight lines as an image to reflect. Draw the mirror line at an angle, touching the letter at one point, on the board.

- Ask someone to draw the reflected letter. Check with a mirror.

- *What can we measure to help us to place the reflections accurately?*

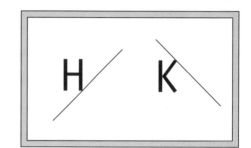

- Draw the reflection for a capital I. Demonstrate using a protractor to measure the angle between the letter and the mirror line. Mark the same angle on the other side of the line. Draw a circle around the angle.

- *How do I know what this angle is? What is this angle?*

- Discuss the fact that there are 360 degrees in the whole turn, and 180 degrees in each straight line (on each side of the mirror line).

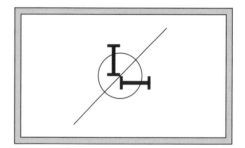

Independent, paired or group work

- Ask the children to draw three different straight-line capital letters, touching a mirror line at an angle.

- They should then exchange papers with a partner and draw the reflections.

- Next, they check with a mirror, then use a protractor to draw the reflections more accurately.

Plenary

- Talk about the reflections.

- *Which were easier to draw than others? What was easier or harder about them?*

- Ask someone to explain how they drew an accurate reflection. Use mirrors to check reflections.

- Enlarge some of the children's work by copying it onto the board.

- Remind the children how to use a protractor to check the angles.

- *How did we know the angles would match?*

Shapes reflected in mirrors at 90 degrees

Advance Organiser

We are going to draw reflections of shapes that have been reflected in two mirrors at right-angles to each other

**Oral/mental starter
pp 177–179**

You will need: pencils, squared paper, mirrors

Whole-class work

- Draw one-quarter of a familiar shape; for example, one-quarter of a sunflower or one-quarter of a pizza. Ask different children to complete each quarter of the remaining shape.

- *How did you decide to draw that? Who thinks that is correct? Who thinks anything different?*

- Use a mirror to check that there are two lines of reflective symmetry by holding the mirror along a horizontal and a vertical line.

- Draw some circles and squares. Ask a child to draw one-quarter of a pattern in either a circle or a square. Ask other children to complete it.

- Show the children how to check, using mirrors.

Independent, paired or group work

- Ask the children to draw two lines of symmetry on squared paper and draw or colour a design in one-quarter.

- They should begin three different designs, then exchange with a partner.

- Then they should draw the reflections of each pattern to complete the square.

- Ask the children to use a mirror to check each reflection.

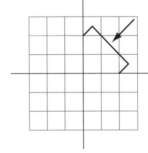 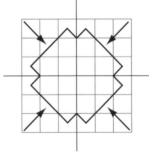

Plenary

- Talk about the patterns.

- *What strategies did you use to make them as accurate as possible?*

- Ask someone who completed a difficult pattern accurately to explain how they went about it.

- If there are errors, see if the person who made the mistake can explain what is wrong.

Making reflections using four quadrants

Advance Organiser

We are going to write coordinates after a shape has been reflected

Oral/mental starter
pp 177–179

You will need: squared paper, pencils, rulers

Whole-class work

- Draw a grid on the board and a quadrilateral in the first quadrant; for example, as shown.

- Ask the children to tell you the coordinates for the corners of the quadrilateral in any order: (2,0) (3,1) (2,4) (1,3).

- *What if we reflect this shape in the y-axis?*

- Ask someone to draw the reflected shape. Ask some children to suggest the coordinates and write them on the board.

- *Now imagine that both shapes are reflected in the x-axis.*

- *Draw the shapes in the third and fourth quadrants.*

- Ask the children to tell you the coordinates of the corners of each shape.

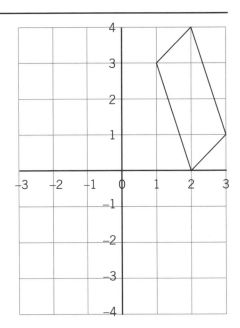

Independent, paired or group work

- Draw a large grid with four quadrants on a large sheet of paper. Ask the children to tell you how to number the axes.

- Decide upon a simple shape that you could draw in one quadrant; for example, a triangle or a square.

- Draw the shape and ask the children to tell you the coordinates.

- Ask them to decide where the shape would be when reflected in the second quadrant of the y-axis. Draw the shape and work out the coordinates of the corners together.

- Ask someone to draw the reflected shapes in the x-axis in the third and fourth quadrants.

- Make sure that everyone can state a coordinate for at least one of the corners.

Plenary

- Ask some of the children to explain how they knew where to place the reflected shapes in each quadrant.

- *How did the numbers of the coordinates change each time? Was there a pattern? How could you use a mirror to check the position of your shapes?*

Finding definitions for congruent triangles

Advance Organiser

We are going to find out what facts you need to know in order to say that two triangles are congruent (identical)

Oral/mental starter pp 177–179

You will need: pencil, paper, rulers, protractors, scissors, 2-D shapes including identical triangles

Whole-class work

- Show the children two identical triangles. Discuss them with the children and demonstrate physically placing one triangle on top of the other.
- *What facts can we state about these triangles?*
- Take ideas from the children; for example, matching sides are the same length, matching angles are equal, and so on.
- Write on the board: *congruent*.
- *Who can tell me what this means?*
- Tell the children that in the context of shapes, *congruent* means *identical*.
- Discuss how they can be sure that the two triangles are congruent.
- *How can we prove they are the same? Who can explain what 'prove' means? How can we use facts about the shapes to be sure they are congruent?*
- *If matching sides are the same length, is it true that the triangles must be congruent? If the matching angles are the same size, is it true that the triangles must be congruent?*
- Look at the possibilities for two sides and their angle.
- *If these two sides of both triangles are equal in length and the angle is the same, is it possible that the third side can be different in length?*

Independent, paired or group work

- Ask the children to work in pairs.
- They should make a statement, or devise a question about congruent triangles.
- *Are triangles always congruent if matching angles are the same?*
- *If two angles of both triangles and the side between the angles are the same, then the triangles are congruent.*
- Ask the children to explore their statement or question by drawing at least three different pairs of triangles.

Plenary

- Collect all the statements that have been investigated. Compare the findings.
- *What did you find out about triangles with equal angles?*
- Establish that two triangles with the same three angles are similar, but can vary in size, so may not be congruent.

Handling Data (1)

Outcome

Children will be able to use the language of probability, present and interpret grouped discrete data on a bar chart and find the mode, range, median and mean of sets of data

Medium-term plan objectives

- Use the language of probability, including events with equally likely outcomes.
- Present and interpret grouped discrete data on a bar chart.
- Use a prepared computer database to compare presentations of data.
- Find the mode and range of a set of data.
- Begin to find the median and mean.

Overview

- Use Venn and Carroll diagrams.
- Use a 0 to 1 probability scale.
- Use grouped data in bar line graphs.
- Find the mode and range of a set of data.
- Find the median and mean of a set of data.

How you could plan this unit

	Stage 1	Stage 2	Stage 3	Stage 4	Stage 5
Content and vocabulary	Venn and Carroll diagrams *Carroll diagram, Venn diagram, group, set, sort, represent*	Probability and chance *fair, unfair, likely, unlikely, likelihood, equally likely, certain, uncertain, probable, possible, impossible, chance, good chance, poor chance, no chance, equal chance, even chance, fifty-fifty chance, outcome*	Discrete data on a bar chart *group, bar chart, block graph, frequency table, label, title, axis, axes*	Range and mode *range, mode*	Median and mean *mean, median, average*
Notes			Resource page A	Resource page B	Resource page C

Venn and Carroll diagrams

Oral/mental starter
pp 179–180

Advance Organiser

We are going to compare Venn and Carroll diagrams

Whole-class work

- Discuss with the children what they like to do as hobbies. Build up a list on the board. Discuss how they could group together some hobbies which are similar; for example, 'reading adventure stories' and 'reading Harry Potter books' could be grouped together as 'reading'.

- *How could we organise this information to make it easier to understand?*

- Discuss Venn diagrams and Carroll diagrams and the characteristics of each. Ask children to help you transfer the list to a Venn diagram.

- *What can you tell me about a Venn diagram? What does it tell us? How can I make one?*

- Encourage the children to describe features, including that the 'universal set' contains everything and the sets inside it must be clearly labelled. Point out that if someone does not belong in any of the sets or groups the class decide on, they are written outside the groups but inside the universal set. Discuss intersections and ask the children to help you build a Venn diagram.

- Repeat the exercise with different data for a Carroll diagram.

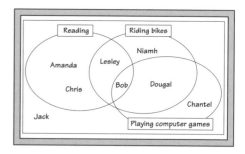

	Likes reading	Does not like reading
Likes football	Amy, William	Ian, Luke
Does not like football	Vicki, Ibrahim	Amarprit, Catriona

Independent, paired or group work

- Ask the children to write five questions about each of the diagrams on the board; for example, *How many children just like reading? Who likes riding bikes and playing football? Which is the most popular hobby?*

Plenary

- Discuss how easy it was to find the information requested on both sheets.

- *Did anyone find one diagram easier to follow than the other?*

- Reinforce the fact that in the Carroll diagram the columns relate to one yes or no question and the rows relate to another.

- Confirm that with the Venn diagram children may be in one or more of the sets and anyone not in a set must belong in the universal set.

Probability and chance

Advance Organiser

We are going to look at the chance of certain outcomes happening

Oral/mental starter pp 179–180

You will need: lots of 1 to 6 dice, playing card, coin or postcard

Whole-class work

- Discuss the chances of a dropped playing card landing on one particular side.

- Encourage lots of vocabulary of chance and probability. Write key phrases on the board.

- Draw a probability line on the board. Ask the children to tell you what it shows and to look particularly at the centre point on the line, which is marked $\frac{1}{2}$.

- Discuss where to write 'chance of playing card landing face up' on the scale. Repeat for chance of card falling to the floor.

- *What is the chance of the card hanging in the air? Where should I write that?*

> It's an even chance, a one in two chance, a fifty-fifty chance, an equal chance, it is equally likely, we would expect it to land this way up once in every 2 goes, there is a probability of 0.5

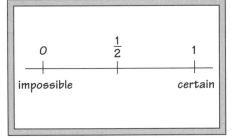

Independent, paired or group work

- Ask the children to draw their own probability scale and write some possible outcomes in the appropriate places on the scale. Ask them to write the following outcomes involving a fair 1 to 6 die.

- *Chance of rolling an even number with one die; rolling an even total with two dice; rolling a multiple of 3 with one die; rolling a 7 with one die; rolling a total that is a multiple of 4 with two dice; rolling a number greater than 3 with one die; rolling at least one number greater than 3 with two dice.*

- When they have done this, give them two 1 to 6 dice and ask them to decide how to test their predictions. Encourage them to roll the dice a number of times and tally the results.

Plenary

- Ask the children to discuss the outcomes of their dice experiment.

- *What did you find out? How did you decide to test your predictions?*

- Discuss how many times the children rolled the dice to test what they thought. Discuss the benefits or drawbacks of a high or low number of rolls.

Discrete data on a bar chart

Advance Organiser

We are going to look at grouped data on bar graphs

Oral/mental starter
pp 179–180

You will need: resource page A (one per child and one enlarged)

Whole-class work

- Tell the children that they are going to present some data to the head teacher on test results. They will need to decide how to present the data.

- Show them the first table on an enlarged version of resource page A, either cut out or with the rest of the page masked.

- *These are the results of the tests. How could we present this data so that someone could see more easily how well the class did?*

- Take ideas from the class. Encourage the children to begin with maths and suggest a bar graph. If necessary, explain what is meant by grouped data and demonstrate breaking the individual scores into ranges such as 1 to 10, 11 to 20, and so on.

- *How else could we group the data? What difference does it make?*

- Encourage the children to make the ranges equal. Work through grouping the data as they decide, using tallying.

- When you have finished, total the tallies. Your results should be the same as the ones printed below.

- Discuss how to use this grouped data to make a bar graph. Ask the children to imagine what it will look like. Brainstorm what they have to include on the bar graph.

Range	Tally	Frequency
1 to 6	II	2
7 to 12	IIII	5
13 to 18	IIII II	7
19 to 24	IIII II	7
25 to 30	IIII	4

- Briefly look at the maths graph on resource page A, pointing out the title, the scale and label, and the ranges written beneath the data columns. Emphasise that these are essential features.

Independent, paired or group work

- Ask the children to complete resource page A, answering the questions in their books and then making a grouped bar graph of the English marks.

Plenary

- *Is this a good way of seeing how well a class has done in a practice test?*

- *How would it look if the data were grouped differently?*

- Make a new frequency chart with the children using a different grouping. Sketch the graph on the board and ask the children to discuss the differences.

PUPIL PAGE

Name: _____

Grouping data on bar graphs

The children in a Year 6 class have started doing practice tests. Here is the first set of results.

The Maths scores have been *grouped* together and put on a bar graph.

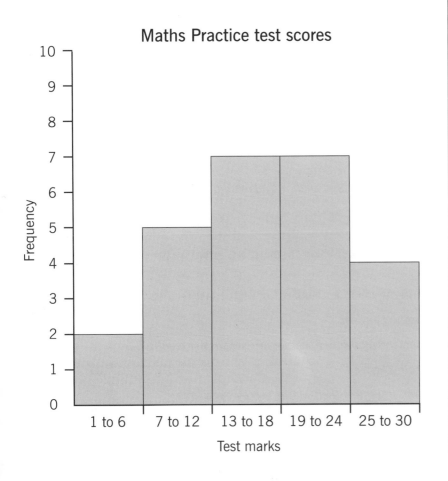

Maths Practice test scores

	Maths	English
Amanda	6	9
Amarprit	20	23
Catriona	8	5
Chantel	19	15
Christopher	13	12
Danny	22	25
Dougal	17	23
Douglas	5	7
Greg	28	26
Hayley	15	13
Ibrahim	20	16
Ian	11	18
Jack	26	24
Joseph	18	11
Justine	12	9
Lesley	8	6
Luke	22	18
Niamh	16	17
Patrick	19	14
Philip	17	20
Rachel	20	23
Richard	28	27
Siobhan	10	4
Vicky	27	24
William	18	22

1   How many children got between 13 and 24 marks?

2   How many children were in the lowest scoring group?

3   How many were in the highest scoring group?

4   How many children got more than 18 marks?

5   How many got less than 13 marks?

6   Use the children's English marks to draw a grouped bar graph showing the English test marks.

7   Compare your *English Test Marks* graph with the *Maths Test Marks* graph. Make up four questions to ask a partner. Remember you have to know the correct answer!

Classworks © Classworks Numeracy author team, Nelson Thornes Ltd, 2003

Range and mode

Advance Organiser

We are going to find the range and mode of some sets of data

You will need: resource page B (one per child and one enlarged)

Whole-class work

● Write on the board: *mode* and *range*.

● *Who can describe what these words mean? How do we find the mode of a set of data? How do we find the range? What are these measures useful for?*

● Look at an enlarged version of resource page B.

● Clarify that the children understand that there are three distinct sets of Maths and English test results.

● Look at the two definitions near the top of the page.

● *The mode of these sets of data give a good idea of how a group of children is doing – it shows the commonest score. When we practise tests we hope that everyone will get better marks so the mode should get higher. Who can explain why?*

● *The range shows how wide the difference is between the poorest and best scores. It could change or stay the same even if everyone improves. Who can explain why?*

Independent, paired or group work

● Ask the children to answer the following questions based on the data on resource page B.

● *Find the range and the mode for each set of Maths test results.*

● *How have they both changed?*

● *Find the range and the mode for each set of English test results.*

● *How have they both changed?*

● *How many children improved their Maths scores each time?*

● *How many children improved their English scores each time?*

● *What is the range of all the Maths tests?*

● *What is the range of all the English tests?*

● If any children finish early, they can make up questions to swap concerning the performance of individual children in the data.

Plenary

● Ask the children to discuss what they found.

● *Does the mode help us to compare the sets of test results?*

● *Have the children as a whole group improved? How can we tell?*

● *Has the range changed for the Maths/English tests?*

● *What does this indicate?*

● *Do these changes imply that the children have all got better or that their scores have simply got closer?*

(**PUPIL PAGE**)

Name: _____

Range and mode

The children in a Year 6 class have now done three lots of practice tests. One way of comparing the sets of marks is to compare the range and the mode.

The *range* is the difference between the highest and lowest values. The *mode* is the most common value.

	First tests		Second tests		Third tests	
	Maths	English	Maths	English	Maths	English
Amanda	6	9	7	11	9	10
Amarprit	20	23	22	25	25	24
Catriona	8	5	10	7	12	9
Chantel	19	15	22	19	26	21
Christopher	13	12	14	15	18	16
Danny	22	25	21	24	26	25
Dougal	17	23	20	23	21	26
Douglas	5	7	11	8	13	9
Greg	28	26	27	24	28	27
Hayley	15	13	18	15	21	19
Ibrahim	20	16	24	19	26	24
Ian	11	18	13	20	19	20
Jack	26	24	26	23	26	28
Joseph	18	11	22	14	21	15
Justine	12	9	15	13	19	16
Lesley	8	6	11	8	12	11
Luke	22	18	23	21	26	23
Niamh	16	17	18	19	23	20
Patrick	19	14	18	16	22	19
Philip	17	20	21	23	25	25
Rachel	20	23	22	24	27	27
Richard	28	27	26	26	29	28
Siobhan	10	4	9	7	11	9
Vicky	27	24	28	22	28	26
William	18	22	24	24	23	25

Classworks © Classworks Numeracy author team, Nelson Thornes Ltd, 2003

Median and mean

Advance Organiser

We are going to find the median and the mean of sets of data

Oral/mental starter pp 179–180

You will need: calculators, resource page C (one per child and one enlarged)

Whole-class work

- Read out the following context to the children.

- *A shop in an area popular with tourists wants to find out the pattern of sales during a full week – which times and days are the best and worst for sales.*

- Discuss with the children why they would want to know this and how they could find out.

- Show the children an enlarged copy of resource page C.

- Introduce the word *median* and write it on the board. Ask the children if they know what it means. Confirm or explain that it simply means the *middle value* in a set of data.

- Demonstrate finding the median of a set of numbers by re-writing them in order, starting with the smallest, and putting a ring around the middle one. Repeat with a set of eight numbers.

- *How can we find the median? There are two middle values.*

- Ask the children for ideas. Lead towards the idea that the middle value will be halfway between the two numbers.

- Discuss the word *mean*.

- *The mean is all the scores added together then divided by the number of scores.*

- Find the mean of the same group of numbers. Demonstrate on a block graph how this works visually.

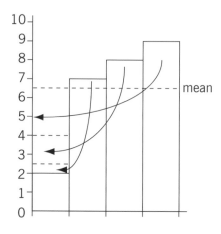

Independent, paired or group work

- Ask the children to complete resource page C. Point out that from 1 to 5 they need to read data down the columns, but for 6 and 7 they need to read data across the rows.

Plenary

- *How do the median and mean help us to interpret the shop's sales figures?*

- Compare the median and mean number of sales for each hour and for each day.

- *The median is the middle number of customers for the hour/day.*

- *The mean is how many customers there would be if they were spread out evenly during the hour/day.*

Name: _____

Shop customers

The owner of a small shop used the clock on its cash till to see how many sales were made each hour. The shop opens every day because it is in a tourist resort. Here is the data collected for a whole week:

		Number of customer sales registered on the cash till							
		1st hour 09.00– 10.00	2nd hour 10.00– 11.00	3rd hour 11.00– 12.00	4th hour 12.00– 13.00	5th hour 13.00– 14.00	6th hour 14.00– 15.00	7th hour 15.00– 16.00	last hour 16.00– 17.00
Day of the week	Sun	12	19	32	54	79	67	42	23
	Mon	43	26	34	38	53	54	41	31
	Tues	18	15	22	31	46	42	35	23
	Wed	21	23	27	48	51	50	38	22
	Thurs	39	28	33	35	58	52	35	32
	Fri	30	22	30	42	63	57	26	34
	Sat	47	42	39	53	56	49	35	31

1 Copy out the number of sales in the first hour for Sunday to Saturday.

2 Re-write the numbers in order, beginning with the smallest.

3 Put a ring around the middle number. This middle number is called the *median*.

4 Repeat this to find the median for the other hours.

5 Find the *mean* for each hour by totalling together the sales for the seven days and dividing it by 7. You can use a calculator to do this.

6 Find the median for each day's sales by reading across each row of the table. *Because there is an even number of values, the median is halfway between the middle two numbers.*

7 Find the mean number of sales for each day. You will need to divide the total sales by 8.

Classworks © Classworks Numeracy author team, Nelson Thornes Ltd, 2003

Handling Data (2)

Outcome

Children will be able to draw conversion charts to help solve mathematical problems

Medium-term plan objectives	• Choose appropriate operations/calculation methods.
	• Explain working.
	• Represent, extract and interpret data in a line graph (for example, a graph to convert miles to kilometres).
	• Recognise that intermediate points have meaning.
Overview	• Construct and understand a conversion chart.
	• Apply data-handling knowledge to solve mathematical problems.
	• Derive information from intermediate points.

How you could plan this unit

	Stage 1	Stage 2	Stage 3	Stage 4	Stage 5
Content and vocabulary	Constructing a conversion chart *chart, diagram, plot, x-axis, y-axis, grid, quadrant, coordinates*	Times-table calculating chart *what could we try next?, how did you work it out?, decide, construct, describe, explain*			
Notes					

Constructing a conversion chart

We are going to make conversion charts

Oral/mental starter pp 179–180

You will need: rulers, squared or graph paper

Whole-class work

- Write on the board: *Fahrenheit* and *°F*.

- *Who knows what degrees Fahrenheit measure? Where have you seen this symbol before? With what units do we usually measure temperature? Does anyone know how to convert Celsius to Fahrenheit?*

- Tell the children that the calculation is Fahrenheit = (1.8 × Celsius) + 32.

- Ask if anyone can think of a way they could help a younger class to convert quickly without having to do this difficult calculation.

- Encourage the children to suggest solutions such as tables or charts. Remind them of, or introduce them to, the idea of a conversion chart. (There are examples on pages 96, 105 and 110.)

- Ask the children how they could make a conversion chart to convert Fahrenheit to Celsius and vice versa.

- Write ideas on the board. Prompt, if necessary, that: the graph could involve four quadrants, so they can convert negative Celsius temperatures easily; they need to think carefully about what scale they will use; they need to work out and mark two or three points, one at each end of the scale they have chosen and join them carefully with a ruler, and so on.

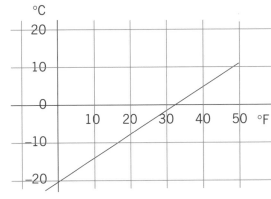

Independent, paired or group work

- Ask the children to construct a conversion chart.

- They should then think up five questions to ask someone about their chart.

Plenary

- Ask a few quick questions and discuss any differences in answer with the class.

- *How accurate are each of your graphs? Why are there differences?*

- Discuss how the children decided to make their graphs and who did things differently.

- Ask a few children to ask some of their questions to the class and agree on answers.

- Point out that intermediate points along the conversion graph *do* have meaning – 1.5 degrees Celsius does have a Fahrenheit equivalent.

Times-table calculating chart

Oral/mental starter pp 179–180

Advance Organiser

We are going to make a graph that will work out multiplication and division equations

You will need: squared paper, rulers

Whole-class work

- Challenge the children to think of a way they could help younger children solve times-table questions.

- Write some ideas on the board. Encourage the children to consider a kind of conversion graph.

- Draw a set of axes on the board and ask the children to help you label them x and y. Write a 0 to 10 scale on the x-axis and a 0 to 40 scale on the y-axis.

- *What do you think I should do next? Why have I numbered the scales in this way? What do you think the conversion graph will look like?*

- Label the x-axis *multiplier* and the y-axis *product*.

- Put a cross on the graph where the line up from 10 on the *multiplier* scale meets the line across from 20 on the *product* scale.

- Draw a straight line to zero in one colour.

- *What does this line show us?*

- Take ideas from the class. Encourage them to read points along the line and relate the multiplier and product. Discuss the relationship between the numbers.

- Write on the board in the same colour as the line: $2 \times$ *table*.

- Ask the children how you should proceed. Encourage them to work out that they need to draw a line for every times-table, mark an end point for each and connect it to zero.

- Repeat for the 3 times-table.

- Demonstrate how it can be used to divide a number by going across from the number on the *product* scale to the line, then down to the answer on the *multiplier* scale.

Independent, paired or group work

- Ask the children to draw their own times-table chart for 2, 3 and 4 times-tables on squared paper.

Plenary

- Ask some quick multiplication and division questions using the children's lines.

- Check any differing answers.

- *How could you help me to work out my $2\frac{1}{2}$ times-table? What about my $1\frac{1}{2}$ times-table?*

Handling Data (3)

Outcome

Children will be able to interpret data, in context, and represent data in a bar chart, grouped appropriately

Medium-term plan objectives	• Extract information from a simple frequency table and convert the data to percentages, using a calculator where appropriate.
	• Interpret a simple pie chart, using fractions or percentages.
	• Solve a problem by representing, extracting and interpreting data in frequency tables and bar charts with grouped discrete data.
Overview	• Interpret data in terms of proportion.
	• Interpret simple pie charts and understand how they are constructed.
	• Use bar charts with grouped discrete data.

How you could plan this unit

	Stage 1	Stage 2	Stage 3	Stage 4	Stage 5
Content and vocabulary	Interpreting data represent, interrogate (data), describe, identify, pick out, discuss, talk about, interpret	Interpreting pie charts percentage, per cent, %, proportion, pie chart	Using bar charts with grouped discrete data group, set		
	Resource page A	Resource pages B and C	Resource page D		
Notes					

143

Interpreting data

Advance Organiser

We are going to decide how to compare sets of data

Oral/mental starter
pp 179–180

You will need: calculators, resource page A (one per child and one enlarged)

Whole-class work

- Show the children an enlarged copy of resource page A.

- *Who thinks skateboarding is more popular with the boys than with the girls in this survey? Why do you think that? Who disagrees? Why do you think that?*

- Encourage them to work out how many children in total answered the survey.

- Point out that it is not fair to say that they are equally popular because although the same number of boys as girls said they liked skateboarding, there are fewer boys than girls in the survey in total.

- *Why does that make a difference?*

- Take ideas from the children and lead them towards the idea that one boy is $\frac{1}{72}$ of all the boys in the survey, whilst 1 girl is $\frac{1}{75}$ of all the girls in the survey.

- *To find whether skateboarding is more popular with boys than girls according to this survey, what do we have to do?*

- Encourage the children to point out that you need to compare the proportions of boys and girls rather than the numbers in each case.

- Suggest that children convert the figures to percentages so they can compare like with like.

- Remind the children of how to convert a fraction to a percentage.

- Ask the children in turn to use a calculator to work out some of the percentages.

Independent, paired or group work

- Ask the children to convert the data on resource page A into percentages and write a new table showing the proportion of boys and girls who enjoy each hobby.

Plenary

- On the board, list the hobbies in order of popularity with the boys.

- Discuss any with identical percentages and decide how to represent their equality in an ordered list; for example, with a curly bracket to indicate that they are 'the same position'.

- List the girls' hobbies in order of popularity and align with the first list.

- As a class, discuss how to combine the data to find the proportion of children in the whole survey who liked each hobby and compare this list with the lists on the board.

Name: _____

Hobbies and pastimes

Hobbies/Pastimes	Boys	Girls
Playing football	54	18
Skateboarding	36	36
Rollerblading	18	33
Cycling	63	54
Computer games	36	42
Using the Internet	45	51
Making things	9	63
Collecting things	18	48

Number of children asked: 72 boys
                               75 girls

Classworks © Classworks Numeracy author team, Nelson Thornes Ltd, 2003

Interpreting pie charts

Advance Organiser

We are going to interpret information from pie charts

Oral/mental starter pp 179–180

You will need: resource page B (enlarged), resource page C (one per child)

Whole-class work

- Ask the children if they know what a pie chart is. Show them an enlarged version of resource page B. Point to each chart in turn.

- *What does this show? Who can tell me what Kevin spends the largest amount of his time doing? How did you find that out?*

- *Who can tell me something about Fang's day? What does he spend the largest amount of his time doing? How did you know?*

- Discuss the different features of the pie chart, ensuring that the children know how to use the key to identify the meaning of each section of the pie chart.

- *How much time in hours does Kevin spend doing homework? How can we work it out?*

- Discuss how to find out with the class. Lead the children towards the idea that *one whole day* is represented by the *whole pie chart* and that each section is a proportion of that day. Remind them, if necessary, that a whole day is equivalent to 24 hours.

- *What does 6% of 24 hours mean? How can we work it out? What is 50% of 24 hours?*

- Work through finding out a couple of percentages of 24 hours.

- *24 ÷ 100 is equivalent to 1% of one whole day. So 6% is this amount multiplied by 6.*

- With the class, look at the different charts for Kevin, his cat and his teacher.

Independent, paired or group work

- Ask the children to complete the problems on resource page C.

- When complete, they can make up their own questions to exchange with a partner.

Plenary

- Compare Kevin's day with that of one or two of the children.

- Compare Fang's day with those of cats that the children have at home.

- Compare the day of Kevin's teacher with a version of your own.

- Look through some of the answers.

- Look at some of the questions suggested by the children after completing question 12.

- *Is it a sensible question? Can there be only one answer? How do we find the answer?*

Name: _____

Different ways to spend a day

Kevin's day

- 2% out on bike
- 6% homework
- 8% on computer
- 2% travelling
- 27% at school
- 39% sleeping
- 4% eating
- 12% watching TV

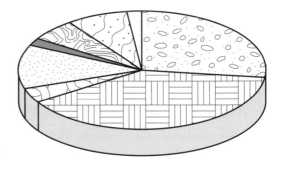

Fang's day

- 1% eating
- 2% asking for food
- 27% prowling
- 20% sleeping on the ironing board
- 15% sleeping on Kevin's bed
- 13% sleeping in basket
- 12% being stroked on lap
- 10% sitting in garden

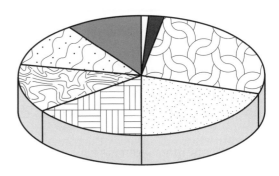

Kevin's teacher's day

- 40% at school
- 8% asleep in front of TV
- 30% asleep in bed
- 8% schoolwork at home
- 7% driving own kids around
- 5% eating
- 2% travelling to school

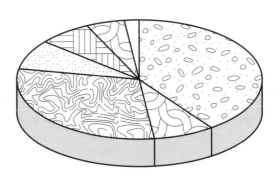

Classworks © Classworks Numeracy author team, Nelson Thornes Ltd, 2003

Name: _____

Interpreting pie charts

Answer the following questions referring to the charts on resource page B.

1 What percentage of the day does Kevin spend awake?

2 What percentage of the day does his cat spend awake?

3 What percentage of the day does Fang spend in the house?

4 What percentage of the day does Kevin spend in the house?

5 Kevin has to travel to school on foot. What percentage of his day does he spend actively?

6 Fang follows the family around asking to be fed. What percentage of the day does he spend actively?

7 What percentage of the day do they each spend on the computer?

8 List their activities in order, starting with the highest percentage.

Compare Kevin's day with his teacher's day.

9 Who gets more exercise?

10 Who spends more time in school?

11 Who spends more time doing schoolwork at home?

12 Who spends more time travelling?

13 Make up some more questions of your own to exchange with a partner. Make sure you know the correct answer.

Using bar charts with grouped discrete data

Advance Organiser

We are going to group data together to make a bar chart

Oral/mental starter
pp 179–180

You will need: resource page D (enlarged)

Whole-class work

- Use an enlarged version of resource page D and ask the children to look at the data on the table.
- Point out that the pocket money amounts may not be accurate, as some children like to exaggerate!
- *What does this table show? How can we present this information more clearly?*
- Take some ideas from the children and write them on the board. Discuss the benefits of each one. Tell the children that you are going to ask them to make a bar graph to represent the data.
- *How can we make a bar graph with this information? What do we do first?*
- Discuss grouping the data with the class. Point out that there is a wide range of amounts of pocket money.
- *What would a graph look like if we did not group the data? How could we group it to make the graph easier to read?*
- Discuss various ways and agree on a method of grouping; for example, as shown in the tally chart below. Ask the class to help you group the data by tallying.

	less than £3	£3–£4	£4.01–£5	£5.01–£10	more than £10
Tally					
Frequency					

Independent, paired or group work

- Ask the children to use the tally chart they have built up to make a bar graph.
- Remind them of the labels, scales, titles and so on that they need to include.
- *How many children say they get less than £10 a week?*
- *Which children say they get £4 a week or less?*
- *How many children say they get more than £4 a week?*
- *Who claims to get the most pocket money?*
- *Write out each child's pocket money in order, starting with the least amount. Find the median and the mode.*
- They can then make up five questions to exchange with a partner.

Plenary

- Discuss the graphs and how children answered the questions.
- *Would the graph be more/less useful if different ranges were used?*

(EXAMPLE)

Pocket money

	Pocket money
Amanda	£2.50
Amarprit	£5.00
Chantel	£12.25
Christopher	£5.00
Danny	£10.00
Dinesh	£4.20
Douglas	£4.00
Greg	£3.00
Hayley	£7.00
Ibrahim	£6.00
Ian	£3.00
Jack	£5.60
Javesh	£3.00

	Pocket money
Justine	£5.00
Lesley	£4.00
Luke	£14.00
Meena	£2.50
Narinder	£4.00
Patrick	£5.00
Piara	£5.25
Rachel	£2.50
Richard	£3.00
Sharma	£8.00
Vicky	£4.00
William	£10.50

Fractions, Decimals and Percentages (1)

Outcome

Children will be able to relate equivalent proportions, in all forms, and solve problems

Medium-term plan objectives	• Consolidate all previous work.
	• Change an improper fraction to a mixed number and vice versa.
	• Recognise equivalent fractions.
	• Reduce fractions by cancelling.
	• Use decimal notation for tenths and hundredths; extend to thousandths for measurements.
	• Know what each digit represents in a number up to three decimal places.
	• Give a decimal lying between two others (for example, 3.4 and 3.5).
	• Understand *percentage* as the number of parts in every 100.
	• Solve simple problems involving ratio and proportion.
Overview	• Convert improper fractions to mixed numbers and vice versa.
	• Find equivalent fractions by multiplying and dividing both the numerator and denominator.
	• Represent the value of decimal numbers to two and measurements to three decimal places.
	• Represent percentages on a 10 × 10 grid.
	• Solve simple problems of ratio and proportion.

How you could plan this unit

	Stage 1	Stage 2	Stage 3	Stage 4	Stage 5
	Improper fractions and mixed numbers	Equivalent fractions	Decimal notation	Percentages	Ratio and proportion
Content and vocabulary	*proper, improper, mixed number, numerator, denominator, equivalent*	*reduced to, cancel, simplify*	*decimal, decimal fraction, decimal point, decimal place*	*percentages, per cent, %*	*proportion, in every, for every, to every, ratio*
	Resource page A			Resource page B	Resource page C
Notes					

Improper fractions and mixed numbers

Advance Organiser

We are going to change an improper fraction to a mixed number and vice versa

Oral/mental starter
p 174

You will need: overhead projector (optional), linking cubes, resource page A

Whole-class work

- Place 12 cubes on an overhead projector. Divide the cubes into three equal sets.

- *What fraction of all the 12 cubes is each set?*

- *How many thirds of the 12 cubes are there in the whole amount?*

- Write on the board: $\frac{3}{3}$ = *1 whole or 1*. Place another set of four cubes beside the $\frac{3}{3}$.

- How many thirds of the 12 cubes are there now?

- Establish that $\frac{3}{3}$ has the same value as 1, and another $\frac{1}{3}$ makes 1 and $\frac{1}{3}$ altogether. There are one-third more cubes than the original 12 cubes. There are four-thirds of the original 12 cubes on the board.

- Write on the board: $\frac{4}{3} = 1\frac{1}{3}$.

- Revise the terms *mixed number* and *improper fraction*.

- *How can we change $\frac{4}{3}$ to a mixed number?*

- *The denominator tells us how many equal parts in one whole.*

- *How do we change $1\frac{1}{3}$ to an improper fraction?*

- Go through other examples as necessary to revise.

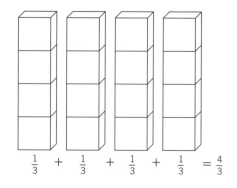

$$\frac{1}{3} + \frac{1}{3} + \frac{1}{3} + \frac{1}{3} = \frac{4}{3}$$

- Ask the children to draw shapes on centimetre-squared paper representing improper fractions and mixed numbers for example, as shown.

- Try other examples, as necessary.

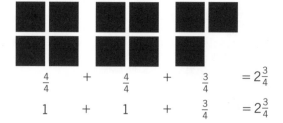

$$\frac{4}{4} + \frac{4}{4} + \frac{3}{4} = 2\frac{3}{4}$$
$$1 + 1 + \frac{3}{4} = 2\frac{3}{4}$$

Independent, paired or group work

- Ask the children to complete resource page A.

- They can then write the following mixed numbers as improper fractions: $\frac{11}{2}$; $\frac{21}{4}$; $\frac{21}{3}$; $\frac{23}{8}$; $\frac{24}{5}$; $\frac{15}{7}$.

Plenary

- Review the activities from resource page A including a discussion of the children's own examples.

Name: _____

Pyramids

Add the fractions together to find the mixed number or whole number at the top of the pyramid. Add each pair of fractions from the left to complete the box above, starting at the bottom of the pyramid. Number 1 is done here as an example:

1

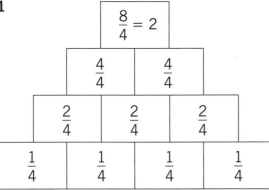

Top: $\frac{8}{4} = 2$

Row: $\frac{4}{4}$ $\frac{4}{4}$

Row: $\frac{2}{4}$ $\frac{2}{4}$ $\frac{2}{4}$

Bottom: $\frac{1}{4}$ $\frac{1}{4}$ $\frac{1}{4}$ $\frac{1}{4}$

2

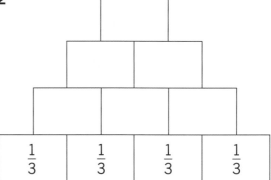

Bottom: $\frac{1}{3}$ $\frac{1}{3}$ $\frac{1}{3}$ $\frac{1}{3}$

3

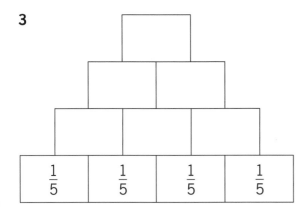

Bottom: $\frac{1}{5}$ $\frac{1}{5}$ $\frac{1}{5}$ $\frac{1}{5}$

4

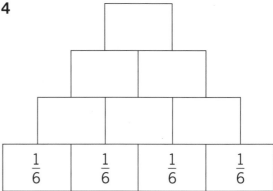

Bottom: $\frac{1}{6}$ $\frac{1}{6}$ $\frac{1}{6}$ $\frac{1}{6}$

5

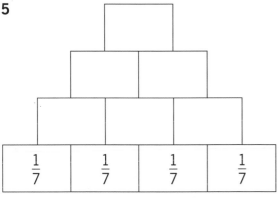

Bottom: $\frac{1}{7}$ $\frac{1}{7}$ $\frac{1}{7}$ $\frac{1}{7}$

6 Make up your own example.

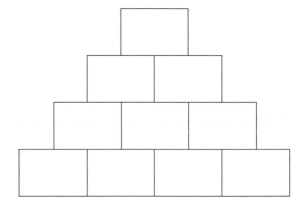

7 Continue by making up your own examples.

Equivalent fractions

Advance Organiser

We are going to recognise equivalent fractions and simplify them by cancelling

Oral/mental starter
p 174

You will need: fraction boards as shown below or other fraction apparatus, linking cubes

---

Whole-class work

- Give each pair of children a fraction board to cut into individual fractions, or give them other fraction apparatus.

- Ask them to match equivalent fractions and record each matching set; for example, $\frac{1}{4} = \frac{2}{8}$, $\frac{1}{2} = \frac{2}{4}$, $\frac{1}{3} = \frac{2}{6}$, $\frac{3}{4} = \frac{6}{8}$, $\frac{2}{3} = \frac{4}{6}$, $\frac{1}{5} = \frac{2}{10}$.

- Ask the children to look for groups of equivalent fractions. Establish the sequence: $\frac{1}{2}$, $\frac{2}{4}$, $\frac{4}{8}$, $\frac{8}{16}$.

- *How is this sequence made?* Point out, if necessary, that the equivalent fractions can be made by multiplying the numerator and denominator by the same number.

- *How would a similar sequence be created starting with $\frac{1}{3}$?*

- Display: $\frac{1}{3}$, $\frac{2}{6}$, $\frac{3}{9}$. *How will this pattern continue? Why?*

- *How would the same pattern continue starting with $\frac{1}{5}$?*

- Draw a diagram on the board as shown.

- *If we record equivalent fractions in this way, what do you notice? What could go in the box that would have the same value as $\frac{6}{9}$ and $\frac{4}{6}$?*

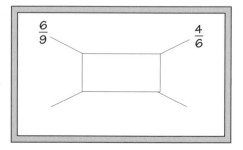

- Ask for ideas. Remind the children that they made the sequence of equivalent fractions in which the numerator and denominator were increasing by multiplying.

- *We can divide the denominator and numerator by the same number – in this case, 2 – and get a fraction of the same value.*

- *This is called 'simplifying' the fraction by 'cancelling'.*

- Ask the children to use linking cubes to demonstrate.

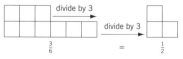

- Point out that sometimes there is more than one step in simplifying; for example, simplifying $\frac{15}{30}$ to $\frac{3}{6}$ and then to $\frac{1}{2}$. Tell the children that they should cancel each fraction until they cannot divide the numerator and denominator again by the same number and get a whole number in both positions.

Independent, paired or group work

- Give the children examples of fractions for them to simplify by cancelling.

Plenary

- Review the process of cancelling to simplify. Ask the children to write examples on the board and discuss how to simplify them. Encourage other children to suggest alternative methods of cancelling the fractions.

Decimal notation

Advance Organiser

We are going to use decimal notation for tenths, hundredths and thousandths

**Oral/mental starter
p 174**

You will need: base 10 apparatus or large sheets of squared paper

Whole-class work

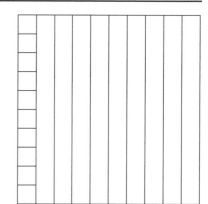

- Draw a 10 × 10 square on a large sheet of squared paper. Mark the ten squares in the first column as shown. Draw three more similar 10 × 10 squares. Alternatively use base 10 apparatus.

- Point to the first column. *What fraction of the whole square is this?*

- *What fraction of one whole square would two whole squares and five columns represent?* ($2\frac{5}{10}$ or 2.5, or $2\frac{1}{2}$)

- *How many of the small squares make up the large square?* (100)

- *What fraction of the large square is each small square?*

- Note that $\frac{1}{100}$ is $\frac{1}{10}$ of $\frac{1}{10}$. Establish that each small square is $\frac{1}{100}$ or 0.01.

- Repeat this with other examples, including numbers containing a zero, such as 2.07.

- Use coins, if necessary, to clarify the value of each digit.

- Extend the use of base 10 apparatus, if available, to include $\frac{1}{1000}$.

- Demonstrate $\frac{1}{1000}$ using a metre stick. Try examples changing metres to millimetres, kilograms to grams, litres to millilitres, and so on.

- Establish the value of each digit in a number with three decimal places. For example, $1.125\,m = 1 + \frac{1}{10} + \frac{2}{100} + \frac{5}{1000}$; $2.235\,kg = 2 + \frac{2}{10} + \frac{3}{100} + \frac{5}{1000}$.

Independent, paired or group work

- Explain how to use 2 mm graph paper to illustrate 1 whole as $\frac{10}{10}$, $\frac{100}{100}$ and $\frac{1}{1000}$.
  Ask the children to represent numbers such as 1.123, 1.521 and 2.136 by drawing around groups of squares.

- Write some decimal numbers on the board and ask the children to write the value of each digit.
  1.35 = □ units + □ tenths + □ hundredths
  1.235 = □ units + □ tenths + □ hundredths + □ thousandths

Plenary

- Review the value of the digits in the examples above. Discuss the value of each 1 digit in the number 1.111.

155

Percentages

Advance Organiser

We are going to write fractions of a whole as percentages

Oral/mental starter p 174

You will need: blank 1 to 100 grid (enlarged), examples of uses of percentage from 'real life' (vitamin boxes [100% of RDA], clothing [55% cotton], and so on), resource page B (one per child)

Whole-class work

- Show the children an enlarged, blank 1 to 100 grid.

- *How many squares on the grid? What fraction of the whole grid is one square? What percentage of the grid is one square?*

- Demonstrate covering numbers, confirming that there are 100 squares on the whole grid and that each square is 1% or $\frac{1}{100}$ of the whole grid.

- Repeat for other proportions; for example, establishing that 100% has the same value as one whole, which has the same value as 1.0, and similarly for 10%, 20%, 50%, 25%, 75% and 45%. Relate the percentages to familiar fractions as well.

- *I have 10p. What percentage is that of £1.00?*

- *I have 20p. What percentage is that of £2.00?*

- *There is one 10p in every £1.00 or 100p, so 10p is 10% of £1.*

- Consider other examples relating to 100 cents in a euro, or 100 cents in a dollar, and so on.

- Establish that *percentage* means the number of parts in every 100 (100% is the whole of anything).

- Look at the labels on clothing and food cartons to see, for example, percentages of cotton and RDA of vitamins. Ask the children to point out those that are the equivalent or familiar fractions.

Independent, paired or group work

- Ask the children to complete resource page B.

Plenary

- Discuss the children's work on resource page B. Ask some children to the front to indicate percentages of the 1 to 100 grid and challenge the class to say what percentage each time.

- Reverse the activity by asking some children to suggest percentages, and challenge others to indicate on the grid what area represents that percentage.

(PUPIL PAGE)

Name: _____

Percentages

Write the fraction, decimal and percentage below each diagram.

1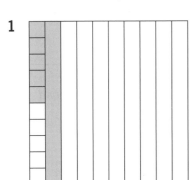

2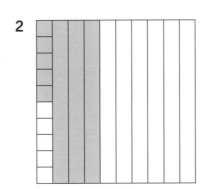

3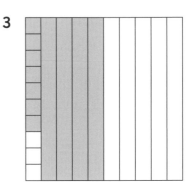

4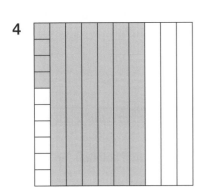

5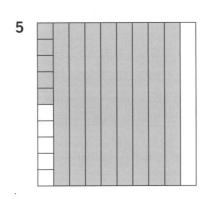

6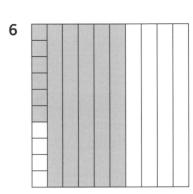

7

8

9 Colour 24% of the grid and write the answer as a fraction, decimal and percentage.

10 Colour 70% of the grid and write the answer as a fraction, decimal and percentage.

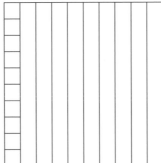

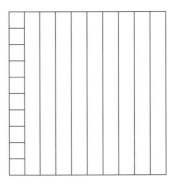

Classworks © Classworks Numeracy author team, Nelson Thornes Ltd, 2003

Ratio and proportion

Advance Organiser

We are going to solve problems involving ratio and proportion

Oral/mental starter p 174

You will need: linking cubes (two colours per child), resource page C (one per child)

Whole-class work

- Give the children a number of linking cubes in two colours. Ask them to make a pattern, as shown.

- *How many black cubes are there? How many white cubes? What if we continued the pattern?*
- Draw out and write on the board: *There are four black cubes to eight white cubes.*
- *For every one black cube, how many white are there? For every two white cubes, how many black are there?*
- *For every one black cube there are two white cubes.*
- If necessary, split the pattern into four sections each with two white and one black.
- *What fraction of the cubes is black?* (four out of 12 or $\frac{1}{3}$)
- *So, one in every three cubes is black.*
- *What fraction of the cubes is white?* (eight out of 12 or $\frac{2}{3}$)
- *So, two in every three cubes are white.*
- *The proportion of black cubes in this pattern is $\frac{1}{3}$. The proportion of white cubes in this pattern is $\frac{2}{3}$.*
- Ask the children to make another rod with a pattern of cubes of two colours; for example, as shown.
- Proceed as before, ensuring an understanding of the part–part relationship (for example, one black for every three white) and the part–whole relationship (for example one in every four is black).
- Ask the children to make two more shapes with the linking cubes; for example, as shown.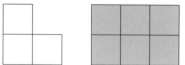
- *To every one white cube there are how many black cubes?*
- *What fraction of the large shape is the small one?*
- *There are two black cubes for every how many white?*
- *What can you say about the large one as compared with the small one?*
- *What proportion of all the cubes is the white shape/black shape?*
- Repeat for other comparisons of shapes.

Independent, paired or group work

- Ask the children to complete resource page C.

Plenary

- Talk through the children's solutions to the problems on resource page C.
- Encourage different descriptions of how they worked out each one.
- Ask the children to describe alternative answers or methods.

(**PUPIL PAGE**)

Name: _____

Proportion problems

Copy and complete these details for each pattern.

For every .... white tiles there are .... black.
For every .... black tiles there are .... white.
In every .... tiles there are .... black.
In every .... tiles there are .... white.
The proportion of white tiles is ....
The proportion of black tiles is ....
The fraction of tiles which are black is ....
The fraction of tiles which are white is ....

Answer the questions each time.

6 There is 1 white square for every .... black squares.
There are .... black squares for every .... white square.
To every .... white there are .... black.
To every .... black there are .... white.
What fraction of the black is the white? ....
What proportion of the total is white?
What proportion of the total is black?

7 There is 1 white square for every .... black squares.
There are .... black squares for every .... white square.
To every .... white there are .... black.
To every .... black there are .... white.
What fraction of the black is the white? ....
What proportion of the total is white?
What proportion of the total is black?

8 Kate shares sweets with her friend. For every 2 sweets she gives to her friend she keeps 3.
She shares out 15 sweets altogether.
   a) How many does Kate have? ....
   b) How many does her friend have? ....
   c) What proportion of the sweets does Kate have?
   d) What proportion does her friend have?

Fractions, Decimals and Percentages (2)

Outcome

Children will be able to order, round and use fractions, and use a calculator

Medium-term plan objectives	• Consolidate all previous work.
	• Order fractions by converting to common denominator, and position them on a number line.
	• Use fractions as 'operators' to find fractions of numbers and quantities.
	• Order a set of mixed numbers or measurements with up to three decimal places.
	• Round a number to the nearest tenth or nearest whole number.
	• Use a calculator effectively.
Overview	• Change fractions to a common denominator.
	• Round decimal numbers to the nearest tenth, or whole, using a number line.
	• Multiply and divide decimal numbers by 10 or 100 using a calculator.

How you could plan this unit

	Stage 1	Stage 2	Stage 3	Stage 4	Stage 5
Content and vocabulary	Ordering fractions *fraction, equivalent, numerator, denominator, greater than, less than*	Fractions of numbers and amounts	Rounding to the nearest tenth or whole *decimal, decimal fraction, decimal point, decimal place, tenth, hundredth, round, nearest*	Using a calculator *calculator, display, key, enter, clear, operation key*	
Notes	Resource page A				

Ordering fractions

Advance Organiser

We are going to order fractions by changing them to a common denominator and position them on a number line

Oral/mental starter p 174

You will need: linking cubes (two colours), resource page A

Whole-class work

- Write on the board: $\frac{1}{2}$.
- *What do we do to the numerator and denominator to make an equivalent fraction?*
- Remind the children, if necessary, to multiply or divide both by the same number.
- Write $\frac{1}{3}$ next to $\frac{1}{2}$.
- *Which is greater? How could we compare them accurately?*
- Take ideas, including, for example, a number line. Point out that we can also compare them by changing them to equivalent fractions with the same denominator.
- Discuss how to model this, such as using linking cubes. With the children, work through converting $\frac{1}{3}$ and $\frac{1}{2}$ into sixths ($\frac{2}{6}$ and $\frac{3}{6}$) and illustrate using two colours of cube.
- Demonstrate using a number line divided into sixths as well.

$\frac{1}{3}\left(\frac{2}{6}\right)$ ... 0 ... $\frac{1}{2}\left(\frac{3}{6}\right)$ ... $1\left(\frac{6}{6}\right)$

- Ask the children to draw their own number lines to record the comparison.
- *So, which is greater, one-half or one-third?*
- *How would we find a fraction which is greater than $\frac{1}{3}$ but less than $\frac{1}{2}$?*
- Establish that it would have to be between $\frac{2}{6}$ and $\frac{3}{6}$.
- Some might suggest *two and a half sixths*.
- Demonstrate with a number line divided into 12 equal parts.

$\frac{1}{3}\left(\frac{4}{12}\right)$ ... $\frac{1}{2}\left(\frac{6}{12}\right)$ ... 0 ... $1\left(\frac{12}{12}\right)$

- Check that the children understand what you have done – converted $\frac{2}{6}$ into $\frac{4}{12}$, and $\frac{3}{6}$ into $\frac{6}{12}$. Remind them that you began with $\frac{1}{3}$ and $\frac{1}{2}$ – these new fractions are equivalent.
- Children may point out that originally you multiplied both parts of $\frac{1}{3}$ by 2, and both parts of $\frac{1}{2}$ by 3, although now you are multiplying everything by 2.
- Establish that $\frac{5}{12}$ is greater than $\frac{1}{3}$ and less than $\frac{1}{2}$.
- Repeat, by comparing $\frac{1}{4}$ and $\frac{1}{3}$, converting both into twelfths, then finding a fraction between them using $\frac{6}{24}$ and $\frac{8}{24}$.

Independent, paired or group work

- Ask the children to complete resource page A.

Plenary

- Review the examples from resource page A.
- Ask the children to help you build a fraction number line from 0 to 1. Discuss how to redraw the line with more divisions, as necessary, to identify fractions 'between' other fractions.

161

(**PUPIL PAGE**)

Name: _____

Ordering fractions

Place the fractions in the correct place on the number lines.

1 $\frac{1}{8}$ $\frac{1}{4}$ $\frac{1}{3}$ $\frac{1}{2}$ $\frac{2}{3}$ $\frac{3}{4}$

2 $\frac{3}{10}$ $\frac{1}{3}$ $\frac{2}{5}$ $\frac{1}{2}$ $\frac{2}{3}$ $\frac{5}{6}$

3 $\frac{1}{6}$ $\frac{1}{4}$ $\frac{1}{3}$ $\frac{1}{2}$ $\frac{2}{3}$ $\frac{3}{4}$

4 $\frac{1}{8}$ $\frac{1}{4}$ $\frac{3}{8}$ $\frac{1}{2}$ $\frac{5}{8}$ $\frac{3}{4}$

Use one of the number lines above to find:

5 A fraction greater than $\frac{1}{6}$ and less than $\frac{1}{5}$

6 A fraction greater than $\frac{1}{8}$ and less than $\frac{1}{4}$

Fractions of numbers and amounts

Advance Organiser

We are going to find fractions of numbers and quantities

Oral/mental starter p 174

You will need: linking cubes

Whole-class work

- Ask the children to build a tower with 12 linking cubes. *How do we find $\frac{1}{4}$ of this tower?*

- Point out, if necessary, that children could divide it into 2 and 2 again, or share out 12 cubes amongst 4 to find $\frac{1}{4}$ of 12.

- *How do we find $\frac{3}{4}$ of 12?* Establish that they find $\frac{1}{4}$ and then multiply by 3. In this case, they build a tower that is three lots of three cubes high, or $3 \times \frac{3}{12}$.

- *What calculation are we performing on 12 to find $\frac{3}{4}$ of 12?*

- Draw out that we divide 12 by 4 and then multiply by 3 to find $\frac{3}{4}$. Finding $\frac{3}{4}$ of a number is the same as dividing the number by 4 and multiplying the result by 3.

- Point out, if no one else does, the connection between the answer (9 cubes is $\frac{3}{4}$ of 12 cubes) and the equivalence of $\frac{9}{12}$ and $\frac{3}{4}$.

- Demonstrate, using cubes, finding $\frac{2}{3}$ of the 12 cubes by calculating $(12 \div 3) \times 2$, then demonstrating by breaking a 12-stick into three groups of four cubes and placing two together to make eight cubes.

- Demonstrate practically using other examples, such as $\frac{2}{5}$ of 10.

- Progress to larger quantities such as $\frac{3}{4}$ of £20.00, £40.00; $\frac{3}{10}$ of 50, 100, 200.

- Stress the importance of setting out the calculation clearly.

- Again, it is worth noting the equivalent fractions $\frac{3}{4} = \frac{15}{20}$.

$= \frac{3}{12}$ or $\frac{1}{4}$

$= \frac{3}{12}$ or $\frac{1}{4}$

$= \frac{3}{12}$ or $\frac{1}{4}$

$= \frac{3}{12}$ or $\frac{1}{4}$

$$\frac{3}{4} \text{ of £20} = (\frac{1}{4} \text{ of £20} \times 3)$$
$$= (£20 \div 4) \times 3$$
$$= £5 \times 3$$
$$= £15$$

Independent, paired or group work

- Set problems of the following type for the children to answer.

- *Which would you rather have, $\frac{3}{4}$ of £12 or $\frac{2}{5}$ of £20?*

- Write more fractions of quantities problems on the board for the children to answer, such as: $\frac{3}{4}$ of £24; $\frac{4}{5}$ of £80; $\frac{2}{3}$ of £60, and so on.

Plenary

- Review examples of calculations with the children, explaining the method.

Rounding to the nearest tenth or whole

Oral/mental starter
p 174

Advance Organiser

We are going to round a number to the nearest tenth or whole number

---

Whole-class work

- Revise rounding measurements in centimetres and millimetres to the nearest centimetre.

- Write on the board: *7.5 cm. How would we write this length to the nearest whole centimetre?*

- Use a number line to remind the children of the convention of rounding up to the next whole number, including rounding 7.5 cm and above to 8 cm.

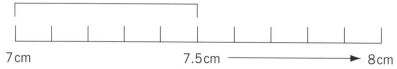

7 cm   7.5 cm ⟶ 8 cm

- Try other examples using measurement; for example, 8.2 cm, 9.7 cm, 10.5 cm.

- Extend to rounding decimal fractions of a metre; for example, rounding 0.55 metres to the nearest tenth (0.6 metres). Ensure the children realise that 0.55 m is the same value as 55 cm. Demonstrate using a number line as shown.

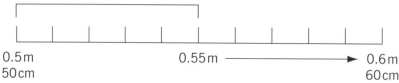

0.5 m   0.55 m ⟶ 0.6 m
50 cm   60 cm

- Write on the board: *0.55 m = 0.6 m to the nearest $\frac{1}{10}$ or 0.1 m.*

- Establish that when rounding to the nearest tenth, we look at the hundredths digit and round up if it is 5 or greater.

- *What would 0.55 m be to the nearest metre?*

- Remind the children that when rounding to the nearest whole number, we look at the tenths digit and round up if it is 5 or greater.

- Practise with other measurements stated to the nearest tenth and whole.

Independent, paired or group work

- Ask the children to draw lines to the nearest $\frac{1}{10}$ of a metre and write their lengths as decimal fractions of a metre: 24 cm, 15 cm, 21 cm, 19 cm, 25 cm.

- They then write each length rounded to the nearest metre and tenth of a metre.

- Write some other lengths for them to round to the nearest metre and to the nearest tenth of a metre: 1.25 m, 3.54 m, 2.75 m, 4.05 m, 10.51 m.

Plenary

- Review examples of the children's work, rounding to the nearest tenth or whole, and agreeing the results.

- Watch out for children rounding to the nearest tenth before they round to the nearest metre; for example, rounding 3.47 as 3.5 and therefore 4, rather than simply rounding 3.47 down to 3, as they should.

Using a calculator

Advance Organiser

We are going to use a calculator to multiply and divide decimal numbers by 10 and 100

Oral/mental starter p 174

You will need: calculators, overhead projector calculator (if possible)

Whole-class work

- Go through the calculator keys on the pad, preferably with an overhead projector calculator to demonstrate; for example, the *clear all* (AC) and *clear entry* (CE or C) keys. Point out that *clear entry* can be used to correct a mistake rather than starting again by pressing *clear all*.

- Key in 1.5.

- *If I multiply the number by 10, what will the answer be?*

- Take some suggestions answer before keying in

- Ask the children to describe in their own words what has happened.

- *How would you get back to 1.5?*

- Ask the children to demonstrate keying in

- *If we multiply by 100, what answer will we get?*

- Key in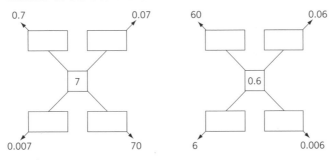

- Again, ask the children to describe what has happened to the digits and try to explain why this has occurred.

- *How would you get back to 1.5 this time?*

- Go through a range of similar examples multiplying and dividing by 10 and 100.

- *What would we have to do to get from 2.6 to 260, 370 to 3.7, 0.5 to 0.05, in one step or operation?*

Independent, paired or group work

- Ask the children to copy and complete the diagrams, as shown. In each box they write the operation they need to key in to change the number in the centre to the number at the end of the arrow.

- They should then make up examples of their own in pairs and solve them.

Plenary

- Ask the children to explain in their own words what happens to the digits in a number when it is multiplied or divided by a multiple of 10.

- Discuss different interpretations and lead the children towards the idea that digits shift along places, rather than 'adding zeroes'.

Fractions, Decimals and Percentages (3)

Outcome

Children will be able to express fractions as decimals and percentages, and find percentages of quantities

Medium-term plan objectives

- Consolidate all previous work.
- Begin to convert fractions to decimals, using division.
- Use a calculator to compare two fractions.
- Express simple fractions as percentages.
- Find simple percentages of whole-number quantities, including calculator use.
- Solve simple problems involving ratio and proportion.

Overview

- Convert fractions to decimals using a calculator.
- Express fractions as percentages using a 1 to 100 grid.
- Calculate percentages of sums of money and quantities.

How you could plan this unit

	Stage 1	Stage 2	Stage 3	Stage 4	Stage 5
Content and vocabulary	Change fractions to decimals *fraction, equivalent, numerator, denominator, decimal, decimal fraction, decimal point, decimal place*	Fractions as percentages *percentage, per cent, %*	Percentages of quantities *investigate, identify, prove*	Ratio and proportion *ratio, proportion, in every, for every, to every, as many as*	
Notes			Resource page A	Resource page B	

Change fractions to decimals

Oral/mental starter
p 174

Advance Organiser

We are going to change fractions to equivalent decimals

Whole-class work

- Write on the board: $\frac{1}{2}$.

- *What does $\frac{1}{2}$ mean?*

- Establish that this means one whole divided into, or by, 2.

- *The following may be considered difficult for many the children, in which case a calculator should be used to divide 1 by 2.*

- Another way of writing 1 is 1.0. *How would you show division of 1 by 2?*

- Set out $\frac{1}{2}$ or $1 \div 2$ as a division.

- Explain this carefully in terms such as:
  2 into 1 does not go. Change 1 into ten tenths. Two into ten tenths is five tenths. The decimal point in the answer is placed directly above that in 1.0.

$$\begin{array}{r} 0.5 \\ 2 \overline{\smash{)}1.0} \end{array}$$

- In the same way as above, or using a calculator, explain $\frac{1}{4}$ as 1 divided by 4.

- In this case, the algorithm is slightly more difficult to explain and once again it may suffice to use a calculator to divide 1 by 4.

- Repeat for $\frac{3}{4}$ as $3 \div 4$.

- Introduce examples of fractions which produce recurring decimals; for example, $\frac{1}{3}, \frac{1}{6}, \frac{1}{7}$ and $\frac{1}{11}$.

Independent, paired or group work

- Ask the children to investigate and record (for example on a table) which decimal fractions recur and which do not. Encourage them to investigate, for example, whether all the sixths recur, all the thirds, all the sevenths, all the elevenths, and so on.

Plenary

- Discuss the use of dots, one above the first and one above the last digit, to denote recurring decimal fractions such as $\frac{1}{3} = 0.\dot{3}$, $\frac{1}{7} = 0.\dot{1}4285\dot{7}$, $\frac{1}{11} = 0.\dot{0}\dot{9}$, and so on.

- Discuss patterns found; for example, $\frac{1}{7}$ recurs after six places of decimals and $\frac{1}{11}$ after two decimal places. Discuss any that do not recur; for example, $\frac{3}{6}$.

- Remind the children how to change a fraction to a decimal – divide the numerator by the denominator.

Fractions as percentages

Advance Organiser

We are going to express fractions as percentages

You will need: 10×10 grid, 1 to 100 grid (one per child)

Whole-class work

- Revise the meaning of percentage, using a 10×10 grid, if necessary, demonstrating that 100% has the same value as one whole. Shade parts of the grid to represent fractions.

- Ask questions such as: *What is a half, 0.25, three-quarters of the grid as a percentage?*

- Use a 1 to 100 grid to ask questions such as: *How many multiples of 3 are there from 1 to 10?*

- *What fraction of the numbers from 1 to 10 is this? What is $\frac{3}{10}$ as something out of 100? What percentage is 30 out of 100 or $\frac{30}{100}$?*

- *How many multiples of 3 are there from 1 to 20? What fraction of the numbers from 1 to 20 is this? What is $\frac{6}{20}$ as something out of 100? What percentage is this of the numbers from 1 to 20?*

- Write these two equivalences on the board: $\frac{3}{10} = 30\%$ and $\frac{6}{20} = 30\%$.

- Ask the children to think of other simple examples where the denominator changes but the percentage stays the same; for example, multiples of 5 from 1 to 10 and 1 to 20.

Independent, paired or group work

- Write some fractions on the board and ask the children to record them as decimals and as percentages; for example, $\frac{1}{5}, \frac{1}{4}, \frac{3}{5}, \frac{3}{4}, \frac{3}{10}, \frac{4}{5}$.

- They then use a 1 to 100 grid to investigate the fraction, decimal and percentage of the numbers from 1 to 100 that are: multiples of 4; square numbers; multiples of 5; and prime numbers.

Plenary

- Go over the examples from the children's work.

- Ask them to describe how they worked out each percentage and what they found.

- Stress that to change a fraction to a percentage it helps to change the denominator to 100 wherever possible beforehand; for example, converting $\frac{1}{4}$ to $\frac{25}{100}$ then to 25%.

Percentages of quantities

Advance Organiser

We are going to find out if some advertisements are correct

Oral/mental starter p 174

You will need: resource page A (one per child)

Whole-class work

- Write on the board the following set of special offers:
  10% extra free – 440g for the price of 400g – biscuits
  5% extra free – 110g for the price of 100g – toothpaste
  20% extra free – 220ml for the price of 200ml – fruit juice
  25% extra free – 625g for the price of 500g – frozen vegetables
  15% extra free – 345g for the price of 300g – mixed nuts

- Tell the children we are going to check these advertisements to see if they are correct.

- Begin with the first example. Ask the children to suggest how they can check the claim. Ask them to describe in their own words what they need to do.

- *What weight (mass) is 100% of the biscuits?* Establish that we are treating 400g as 100%.

- *The advertisement claims that 10% extra is free. What fraction is 10%?*

- Revise the fact that 10% is $\frac{10}{100}$, which is the same as $\frac{1}{10}$ or 0.1.

- *What do we need to calculate?* Establish that it is 10% extra on the original 400g.

- *How do we find 10% of 400g?* Calculate: $\frac{1}{10}$ of 400g = 40g.

- *Is the claim in the advertisement correct?*

- Repeat for the second claim.

- Some the children will see right away that the claim is inaccurate since 10g extra is 10% of 100g.

- Go through the other examples using, for example, 10% as the basis for calculating 20%, 25% and 15%.

- Try an example involving 12.5% of a quantity by finding 10% plus one-quarter of 10%.

- *The percentages we have been looking at are quite easy to work with. What if we had to work out the following: 18% extra free – 260ml for the price of 220ml?*

- Work through this example agreeing that a calculator can be used for this calculation.

- Discuss whether the claim is correct – the answer is 39.6ml extra free, so the claim is *approximately* correct, but not *exactly*.

Independent, paired or group work

- Ask the children to complete resource page A.

Plenary

- Review the calculations from resource page A.

- Ask the children to explain their methods paying particular attention to the way the calculation has been set out.

(**PUPIL PAGE**)

Name: _____

Does it ad. up?

Calculate and decide whether the claim in the advertisement is correct in each case. Show your working.

---

1 70% extra free – 510cm for the price of 300cm – ribbon

---

2 25% extra free – 375ml for the price of 300ml – bottled water

---

3 12.5% extra free – 900g for the price of 800g – potatoes

---

4 15% extra free – 460 square metres for the price of 400 square metres – carpet

---

5 30% extra free – 395g for the price of 300g – lentils

---

6 40% extra free – 4.2m for the price of 3m – rope

Make up two advertisements of your own.

Classworks © Classworks Numeracy author team, Nelson Thornes Ltd, 2003

Ratio and proportion

Advance Organiser

We are going to solve problems involving ratio and proportion

**Oral/mental starter
p 174**

You will need: resource page B (one per child)

Whole-class work

- Present the children with a story. Ask them to listen carefully and picture in their heads what is happening.

- *Imagine two brothers called Jake and Milo. They are not treated equally. For every £1 Dad gives to Jake, he gives £3 to Milo. Both brothers save all their money in a bank account. Milo clearly saves more than Jake. I would like you to help me work out how their savings grew.*

- Draw a chart on the board as follows.

- Ask the children to discuss what the chart tells them. Write ideas on the board.

Jake	Milo	Total
£1	£3	£4
£2	£6	£8
£3	£9	£12

- *For every £1 Jake saves, Milo saves £3.*

- *What do you notice about Milo's savings? The amount is always a multiple of 3.*

- *What do you notice about the total? The total is always a multiple of 4.*

- *By the time Jake has saved £7, how much will Milo have saved?*

- *If they saved £24 altogether, how much of that is Jake's and how much is Milo's?*

- Discuss the method the children use to answer the last question.

- Suggest dividing the £24 into four amounts of £6 and giving one amount to Jake and three amounts to Milo.

- Write up the statements: *For every £1 Jake gets, Milo gets £3. Jake gets £1 in every £4 and Milo gets £3 in every £4.*

- *What fraction of the savings does Jake/Milo get?*

- Repeat for a similar problem. *Imagine this time that for every £1 Jake gets, his brother gets £5.*

- Try other ratios such as 2:3.

Independent, paired or group work

- Ask the children to solve the problems on resource page B.

Plenary

- Review the problems in the activity, setting out a table and discussing the solutions.

- Using a ratio of 1:4, ask the children to work out the missing numbers in the following table.

Red paint	White paint	Total
1	4	5
?	?	10

(PUPIL PAGE)

Name: _____

In proportion

Solve each problem by drawing a table to help you. Answer the questions.

1   A painter mixes one tin of yellow paint with two tins of blue. She needs 12 tins of paint altogether. How many tins of yellow paint does she need?

2   Jim shares sweets with a friend. He gives one sweet for every three which he keeps. He shares out 20 sweets. How many does his friend receive?

3   There are four chocolates to every two toffees in a box of 30 sweets. How many chocolates are there?

4   In a swimming club there are two boys for every three girls. There are 35 members altogether. How many girls are there?

5   Jane saves £2 per week and her sister saves £3 per week. Their total savings is £25. How much has Jane saved?

6   A tiler puts tiles on a wall. For every blue tile there are three pink tiles. There are 32 tiles on the wall. How many are blue? How many are pink?

7   For every green bead on a necklace there are five red ones. There are 24 beads on the necklace. How many red ones are there?

8   In a choir, there are three boys for every two girls. There are 24 boys in the choir. How many girls are there?

9   Make up two similar problems of your own and ask your neighbour to solve them.

Oral/mental starter ideas

Properties of number

What's the value?

Write a number on the board, with any number of digits, and ask the children to state the value of a particular digit if the number were multiplied or divided by 10, 100 or 1000; for example, *My number is 340. What value would the digit 4 have if I multiplied my number by 100? My number is 67,013. What value would the digit 1 have if I divided my number by 1000?*

Multiples and factors

Challenge the children to state the lowest common multiple of a pair of numbers, or the highest common factor of a pair of numbers; for example, *What's the lowest common multiple of 8 and 14? What's the highest common factor of 36 and 92?* Alternatively, ask the children to state a number as a multiple of prime factors.

Negative numbers

Ask a variety of negative number problems, such as, *What is nine more than negative three? Twelve less than eight?* and so on. Alternatively, ask some contextual questions, such as, *The temperature in a room is 18 degrees Celsius. It rises 8 degrees then falls 10 degrees. What is the temperature now? The pass mark in a test is 30 marks. A teacher records the marks of a group in relation to the pass mark: +3, −4, +1, 0, −1. How many passed the test? Who scored the most? Who scored the least?*

Rounding

Ask the children to estimate some quantities rounded to the appropriate amount; for example, *How many grains of sand in a 5 litre bucket, to the nearest 10 000? How many people in the UK, to the nearest million?* Discuss different estimates. Alternatively, ask the children how they would estimate (that is, rounded to the nearest value) various quantities: the distance from the Earth to the Sun, the perimeter of the school playing field, and so on.

Estimating

Draw a number line on the board and number each end; for example, 0 and 10 000, or −50 and 0, or 0 and 1. Point to positions on the line and ask the children to estimate the value of that point on the line.

Negative number lines

Brainstorm uses of positive to negative number lines; for example, thermometers, historical timelines that include dates BC. *When do we need numbers less than 1?* For example, owing money, countdown to launch and so on. Ask the children to draw and label some number lines that include positive and negative numbers. Notice 0 and the numbers on each side of it.

Fractions, decimals and percentages

Fractions of...

Ask quick questions involving finding fractions of whole numbers or quantities; for example, $\frac{3}{10}$ of 2 metres, $\frac{23}{100}$ of £3, $\frac{7}{10}$ of 4 litres, and so on. Extend to asking questions such as: *What fraction of 1 year is four weeks? What fraction of 10 kilometres is 200 metres?*

Fractions of fractions

Ask the children some 'fractions of fractions' questions based on their knowledge of equivalence; for example, *What is half of a half? What is half of one-quarter? What is one-sixth multiplied by 3? What is one-tenth divided by 10? How many halves in $4\frac{1}{2}$? How many thirds in $6\frac{1}{3}$?*

Equivalents

Write a fraction on the board, such as $\frac{47}{100}$, and ask the children to suggest other ways you could write this number, such as $47 \div 100$, 47%, 0.47, and so on. Repeat for improper numbers such as $\frac{74}{6}$, or begin with a percentage, a decimal, and so on.

Decimal rounding

Call out a decimal number, such as 7.103, and ask the children to say the value of each digit. Repeat for other numbers. Then ask the children to round the number to the nearest whole number, revising the fact that, for example, 3.5 is rounded up to 4. Repeat for rounding to the nearest tenth. Alternatively, ask the children what operation they could perform to change the number in one step to the next tenth; for example, *Change 1.24 to 1.3 in one step.*

Ratios and proportions

Write a ratio, proportion statement or pattern on the board, for example, *In every 3 days there is 1 rainy day.* Ask questions based on the statement or pattern, for example, *How many rainy days in 21 days? How many days would not be rainy? What about in 25 days, what would you expect then?*

Addition and subtraction

How many more?

Write a target number on the board, for example, 7003. Call out a smaller number the other side of a hundreds boundary, for example 2897, and ask how many more to make the target number. Change the numbers and repeat. Alternatively, write a large number with no hundreds difference, such as 6043, on the board, and say a number just less than a hundreds number, for example, 3889. The children have to add the difference to find the new number. Alternatively, ask some decimal questions, such as, *How many more do I add to 3.64 to make 4? What do I add to 2.43 to make 2.5?* and so on.

0.9, 1.1, 1.9, 2.1...

Ask questions adding or subtracting 0.9, 1.9, 2.9, and so on, or 1.1, 2.1, 3.1, and so on; for example, 1.4 + 2.9, 56 − 3.1, and so on. Show a 1 to 100 grid as support if necessary, pointing down the columns as you ask the questions or asking the children to the front to demonstrate using the grid or to describe how to use it.

Multiplication and division

Squares and tables

Practise the children's times-tables up to 12×12, or their knowledge of squares up to 12 x 12, as a class. Then ask a mixture of rapid questions involving appropriate tables and squares. *What is 0 times 11? What is 11 times 12? What is 7 squared? What is 9 squared? What is 11 squared?* Alternatively, challenge the children to derive squares of multiples of 10, such as 20 squared, 50 squared, 120 squared and so on.

Mental or written?

Ask two children each to think of a one-, two- or three-digit number (include decimal numbers alternatively). They write their numbers down on a piece of paper and simultaneously reveal them to the class. The class then decide if they can find the product in their heads or on the board. Discuss how to solve the equation; for example, 11×100 or 23×12 might be calculated quickly using a mental method, whereas 127×218 might be better with a written method or using a calculator. After a few goes, discuss what sorts of calculation are best done with each method. Include discussions about how different children may prefer to use different methods for the same calculation.

Remainders and quotients

Ask the children a mixture of division questions, some of which require answers to be given with remainders. Discuss quick ways of working these out; for example, working out $41 \div 4$ by rounding 41 down to 40 and showing the remainder of 1. Extend to asking the children to state quotients as decimal fractions, such as, *What is 6 divided by 4? What is the decimal answer? (1.5).* Alternatively, include some rounding, in context, such as, *Boxes of eggs hold six eggs each. How many boxes do I need to hold 38 eggs? How many full boxes are there?*

Make it easy!

Write a 'difficult' mental calculation on the board; for example, 7×24, 25×18, $\frac{1}{6}$ of 333, $\frac{1}{12}$ of 45, $\frac{1}{20}$ of 370, and so on. Ask the children to suggest how to make it easier; for example, finding the 24 times-table by repeated doubling of the 6 times-table, finding multiples of 25 by multiplying by 100 and dividing by 4, finding one-third and halving, finding one-third then dividing by 4, finding one-tenth and halving, and so on.

Solving problems

Which operation?

Write some 'missing operation' calculations on the board and ask the children to say, without working out the answer, what the operation must be; for example, write 42.7 ? 34.1 = 76.8, or 27 ? 26 = 702. Ask the children to explain how they knew what the operation had to be.

Arrange it

Write a selection of digits on the board; for example, 7, 4, 0, 6, 4, 1, 3, 9. Ask the children to discuss, in groups, how they could arrange these digits in a calculation to make the largest sum, largest product, smallest difference, and so on. Place restrictions on the size of the numbers, as appropriate, and indicate whether decimal numbers are allowed. *What if one number had to have only two digits? What if both numbers had to be less than 5000?*

The Bureau

Write some simple currency conversion rates on the board (you could base them on today's newspaper rates); for example, £1 is worth $1.64, 193 yen, 6.82 shekels, 47.92 roubles, and so on. Ask quick conversion questions based on these rates, such as, *About how many UK pounds do I need to buy 150 roubles? About how much would I pay in UK currency to buy 1000 yen?*

15% off!

Ask some questions involving the children finding percentages of amounts of money: for example, *A car costs £4000. The deposit payable is 15%. How much is the deposit?* Repeat for different amounts, and for 5%, 10%, 15%, 20%, 25%, 50% deposits, and so on. Alternatively, ask questions based on sale prices of 50% off, 25%, and so on. Extend to finding prices with or without VAT (17.5%).

General statements

Write a general statement on the board using letters; for example, $a = 2 \times b$. Challenge the children to 'decode' the statement for different values of a, and rephrase it in their own language, or to think of a number story to go with it; for example, *Jenny's pocket money is £a per week. Her older brother gets twice as much each week. If Jenny gets £1 per week, how much does her brother get? What if she gets £2 per week?* Alternatively, start with the 'story' statement and ask the children how they could write this as a general statement. Extend to statements such as $a = (3 \times b) + 4$, and ask the children what sequence this produces for values of a from 1 to 10.

How many questions?

Ask the children to find, for example, as many ways as they can of making each number from 1 to 40 using the digits 1 to 9 once only, or from 0 to 10 including tenths numbers, using certain mathematical operators, such as just + and =, or + or × and =, and so on. Alternatively, write a missing-number statement on the board, such as $\bigcirc + \triangle + \square = 2.8$, and ask the children to suggest different ways to complete the statement correctly.

Find the numbers

Challenge the children to find, for example, three consecutive numbers with a sum of 264, two consecutive numbers with a product of 4556, and so on. Ask them to suggest their own 'find the numbers' problem for the rest of the class. Make sure they can solve it themselves first! Alternatively, introduce a game involving, for example, digital roots (adding the digits of a number until you get to a single digit; for example, to find the digital root of 438 we add 4 + 3 + 8 to get 15, then add 1 + 5 to get 6). *How many three-digit numbers can you find with a digital root of 5? What about a digital root of 8?*

Measures

Time across the world

Ask some time questions using time zones; for example, *San Francisco is 8 hours behind GMT. If a plane leaves London at 14:30 and takes 11 hours to get there, what is the time locally when it lands in San Francisco?* Discuss methods for solving these problems, including using a time line. Alternatively, pick several locations around the world, write their time zones on the board and ask 'time of day' questions, such as, *It is early morning in Sydney. What time of day is it in London? What about in Mexico City? If it is dark in Paris, is it more likely to be light or dark in Beijing?*

How many, how far?

Ask some mixed-unit questions based on different measures; for example, *If a bucket holds 8.25 litres of water, how many full 450 ml jugs would it take to fill the bucket? Scott walks 275 metres. He then gets a bus for two and a half kilometres, gets on his bike and rides for 1200 metres. How far has he travelled altogether?* Repeat for other similar measures questions.

Sensible measures

Give the children some options of very small heights, weights, lengths, capacities, and so on, that they might need to estimate or measure – how would they do this accurately? For example, *How would you measure: the mass of a feather, the length of a full stop, the time it takes to blink, the thickness of a hair?* and so on. Take lots of ideas and discuss how they would, or would not, work.

Equivalences

Play a 'how many?' game involving imperial and metric units; for example, *How many miles are about the same as 10 kilometres? How many grams in a pound?* Brainstorm approximate equivalences; for example, a mile is about 1.5 kilometres or 1600 metres, a pint is about 570 ml, a gallon is about 4.5 litres, a litre is about 2 pints, a kilo is about 2.2 pounds, 30 grams is about 1 ounce, and so on.

Shape and space

Triangle facts

Revise the names and definitions of scalene, isosceles, right-angled and equilateral triangles. Ask the children to draw each one on the board. *Which triangle has the largest angle? Which has the smallest? Find an acute angle. Find an obtuse angle.* Ask a child to define 'acute' and 'obtuse'. Find right-angles.

Quadrilateral facts

Revise the names of quadrilaterals. Ask a child to draw each one. Define each shape. *Is a rectangle a parallelogram? Is a trapezium a parallelogram? Can a square be a rhombus? Why is a kite not a rhombus?*

Tessellations

Look for, and recall, tessellating patterns in the environment; for example, floor tiles, roof tiles, paving stones, diamond window panes, a honeycomb, scales on reptiles, woodblock floors. Ask the children to draw tessellating patterns that they have seen. Note the individual shapes. *Are they always regular shapes?*

Pentominoes and nets

Revise pentominoes – shapes made from five adjoining squares. Ask someone to draw a pentomino. *If we cut it out, could it be folded into an open cube?* Draw another pentomino that could be folded into an open cube. Cut out some pentominoes from 2 cm squared paper and ask someone to fold them into open cubes if possible. *If you have four of the squares next to each other in a larger square, does that help or hinder you in folding an open cube?*

Angles and triangles

Revise what you know about angles in triangles. Ask the children to name and define the different kinds of triangles. Draw an example of each type. Mark all the acute, obtuse and right-angled angles. Mark angles that are equal in each type of triangle. *Is it possible to have two obtuse angles in one triangle? Why is that? Is it possible to have three acute angles in one triangle? Why is that? Is it possible to have more than one right-angle in a triangle?*

Turns

Revise clockwise and anticlockwise turns. Use an object such as a shoe. Ask a child to hold it straight up, towards the ceiling. Ask another child to move the child's arm through 90 degrees clockwise. *How has the shoe changed its position?* Ask the class to predict where the object will be if turned through a further 90 degrees clockwise. Ask a different child to move the child's arm. *Were you right?* Use a different object and move through 90 degrees anticlockwise. Each time notice how the object changes its orientation.

Translations, rotations, reflections

Revise translations, rotations and reflections. Draw a capital letter D on the board or use cut-out or wooden letters attached to the board with Blu-Tack. Ask the children to draw: three horizontal translations, a variety of reflections, and some rotations through 90 degrees. Repeat with other letters, such as C, K or S.

Mirror lines

Use straight-line letters as shapes to reflect in a mirror line. Draw some letters parallel to the line, and others at right-angles to it. Ask different children to draw the reflection each time.

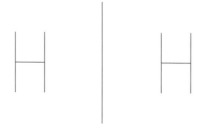

Ask the children to draw a letter and a mirror line and name someone else to draw the reflection. Draw attention to the distance of the reflection from the mirror line.

Lines of symmetry

Revise symmetry by asking the children to name objects and shapes that have one line of symmetry. Make a list. *Is the line of symmetry horizontal or vertical?* Ask them to think of shapes and objects that have both horizontal and vertical lines of symmetry; for example, circles, rectangles, some flags, doors, windows.

Quadrant grids

Draw a grid with four quadrants. Remind the children which is the first, second, third and fourth:

second quadrant	first quadrant
third quadrant	fourth quadrant

Label the x (horizontal) and y (vertical) axes. Ask the children to tell you where to write 0 and how to number each axis with positive or negative numbers. Practise finding given points; for example, $(-2,3)$.

Equal sides and angles

Recall facts about triangles. *What are equal in equilateral triangles? In isosceles triangles?* Draw the triangles and ask the children to mark equal angles and equal sides:

Handling data

Conversion graphs

Ask the children to tell you a conversion rate they know; for example, there are about 8 kilometres to every 5 miles; there are about $1.6US to £1UK. Discuss how easy it is to find other values; for example, how many miles there are in 71 kilometres, how many pounds in $25? With the children, discuss how to make a straight line conversion graph, including appropriate methods to draw the line, scales, labels, and so on. Ask different children to say an amount to convert and ask the children to use the graph to find the answer.

Probability

Draw a probability line on the board as shown, from *no chance* to *certain*. Point to different areas and ask the children to suggest an event with that probability. State different events and ask the children to place them on the probability line.

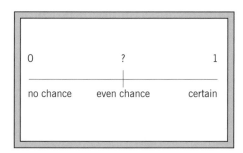

Discuss *even chances,* and so on, and discuss some equally likely events; for example, rolling different numbers on a fair die. *What is the chance of rolling a 1 or a 2? What about the chance of not rolling a 5?*

Grouped data

Collect some quick data from the class; for example, how old the children are in years and months. Working with the class, display this as ungrouped data on a bar chart (one column for 10 years 10 months, one for 10 years 11 months, and so on). *What would happen if I grouped the data for every two months? What about every three? How else could I group it? How would the graph be different? How would the data be different?* Discuss how the collected data would be the same, but the presentation of it might affect how it appears.